FOUR LONG DAYS:
Return to Attica

September 9-13, 1971

Story by
Anthony R. Strollo

As Told to and Written by
Dorothy Wills-Raftery

D1496445

Library of Congress Catalog Card Number: 94-79976.

ISBN # 0-9643795-0-3

Printed in the United States of America.

Background cover photo by Thomas A. Strollo

CONTENTS

This story is dedicated
to all who served
in the line of duty
during the Attica Prison
Riot of 1971.

FOREWORD

The Attica rebellion was portrayed as a clash between two sharply defined forces, the rebels and the authorities.

But there were many lives caught in between.

October 4, 1971   *The New York Times*
New York   "The Attica Revolt: Hour-By-Hour"
                Joseph Lelyveld, Francis X. Clines,
                Michael T. Kaufman and
                James M. Markham

This story is based upon true events as retold by Anthony R. Strollo.

*Names have been changed to protect the privacy of those who were involved.

PREFACE

On September 9, 1971 the Attica State Prison Riot began. In D-Yard, 1,281 inmates held 38 Correctional Officers and civilian employees hostage. One of those hostages was Correctional Officer Frank Strollo. By coincidence, his brother, Anthony Strollo, was one of the New York State Troopers assigned to the hostage rescue detail. This is Trooper Strollo's story of the four long days of waiting before they, the State Police, were given the word to go in , rescue the hostages and restore order.

"Forty-three people died as a result of the Attica Prison Riot. And why did they die? The riot was a great tragedy for many families, yet many people will forget the bloodiest prison riot in American history. But for others who were part of this history-making event, it will never be forgotten."

1990   Anthony R. Strollo
New York

PROLOGUE

JUNE 1971: The Dream

* * *

The steady whir of helicopter blades cutting the air sounded prominently above shouts and gunfire from below in what appeared to be a yard...a prison yard. Inmates were running rampant raising handmade weapons of glass and steel, striking other inmates and uniformed Correctional Officers.

It was a horrific scene.

New York State Troopers clad in riot helmets and standard, but I.D.-less uniforms, began to flood the yard trying to bring the maddening scene under control. Yells and groans of death could be heard. The smell of blood hung thick in the air. The scene began to blur together. Everyone was faceless. The scene became senseless, but real.

One Trooper paused amidst the confusion to frantically search his surroundings. He climbed up what appeared to be a ladder over a wall. He then turned and his face became all too clear....

"Tony!" Marie* screamed out into the still darkness of the bedroom as her head shot up from the pillow, her thin body soaked in sweat as her heart palpitated wildly. Automatically, she reached over to touch her husband. Feeling his sleeping body next to hers, Marie sighed. She sat erect while trying desperately to decipher and understand her dream, while at the same time wanting to block it out of her mind. As her head cleared, she began to realize that it was not a dream at all. It was more like a nightmare.

"Oh my God," she whispered to herself as she ran her hands up and down her bare arms. "Oh my God, no." Groping for the alarm clock on the nightstand next to her, she noted that it was only 3:00 a.m. Leaning back over, she once again tried to wake her husband who had finished his shift only a few hours earlier. "Tony, are you awake?" she whispered.

"Mmmm."

"Tony, I've had another one of my dreams. This one was terrible. I don't understand it," Marie said still visibly shaken from the uneasy feeling the dream left with her. "Tony, can you hear me? Tony?" she called as she anxiously shook him.

Tony stirred and sleepily groaned his reply. "Mmm-hmm."

Marie sighed as she dropped back against her pillow and rubbed her forefinger to her temple, feeling the steady pulse pound. She knew a headache was coming on. "I just can't imagine what it really was about. It's just... turmoil. It was awful." Her voice was a mere whisper. "My God, it was pure chaos."

Marie tried to shake off the chill that raced through her body, her skin pricking into thousands of tiny goosebumps. "I just don't understand this one, Tony," she said as she covered her face with her hands as if to block out the vision. "Everybody was just all over the place. And...I, I know it was at a prison."

The one thing about the dream that Marie could vividly recall was what frightened her the most. "I remember seeing you go up over a wall...the prison wall," she said as her voice quivered.

Marie glanced over at Tony's sleeping form. Rolling onto her side, her body still trembling as she listened to her own heart pounding, she slipped an arm around his body hoping to feel his strength. For Marie, sleep would now be an impossible feat.

She feared her dreams...they almost always came true.

2

On Wednesday, September 8, 1971, a misunderstanding arose over some...activity between two inmates in A Yard. A Lieutenant approached one of the inmates and gave an order. The inmate disregarded the order and ended up striking the Lieutenant twice. Another seasoned Lieutenant entered the yard in order to diffuse the situation but to no avail. Both officers left and decided to handle the matter later.

After the inmates were locked in that night, corrections officers went to the cells of the offending inmates and removed them to HBZ (solitary confinement). The companies of those prisoners rose in uproar and an inmate threw a can from his cell which struck a corrections officer in the head.

1987
New York

History of the New York State Police 1917 - 1987
"Attica - 1971 - LeBastille Extraordinaire"
Sgt. Pamela T. Shelton

Thursday, September 9, 1971....On their way to the Mess Hall for the second breakfast sitting, the men of 5 Gallery...burst into rebellion.

Surging into a vestibule on the main floor of their cellblock and a passageway that runs through the yards, the inmates easily overpowered the five guards they found in their way. An inmate who looked on saw one guard clinging to the gate of the vestibule, holding himself upright as the inmates beat him fiercely.

The uproar in the vestibule could be seen plainly by a guard who was protected by a series of electric gates that he controlled. "Help! Help! They need help in A Block," he shouted into a phone.

By this time rebel inmates had stormed the 100 yards down the narrow passageway to "Times Square", the critical intersection where the four yards met. There was a single guard on duty at a manual gate that always was left open during the breakfast hour.

The guard was unable to secure the gate against the inmates. As he was subdued, his skull was fractured in two places.

Having taken Times Square the inmates had easy access to B, C, and D Cellblocks. Raiding parties moved off in three directions.

Not all inmates were eager to be "liberated". In 12 Gallery of A Block, a group of 30 prisoners - blacks as well as whites - obtained a set of keys and locked themselves into their cells. Rebel inmates, armed with pipes and razors, found another set of keys and opened the cells, announcing in tones that did not invite disagreement, "Everybody's going down to D Yard."

Four hours later, when a detachment of State Police resecured A Block, seven inmates were found hiding under bunks.

A convict who had served 11 years of a 30-year sentence for armed robbery, had a parole hearing coming up in two weeks and was eager to disassociate himself from the uprising. Seeing the inert form of the guard with the fractured skull and noticing that he was bleeding from the ears, the prisoner suggested to a prisoner who was one of those who assumed a position of authority, that the guard be turned over to the authorities because his life was in danger.

The officer's body was then carried on a mattress to a gate that separated rebel territory from the rest of the prison .

(The guard would later die in a hospital from those injuries he sustained to his skull.)

A rough social order was created. Particular hostages had been sought out by inmates with scores to settle and beaten severely.

One guard whose arm was fractured was a particular target. The beatings stopped as security guards were selected from the cells and posted over the hostages who had been stripped, bound and blindfolded, but assured that their guards were there to protect them.

Some of the inmates were old hands at manifestoes. At the start of July, a statement of 27 demands - covering the grievances that were to be aired again - had been sent to the new Commissioner of Corrections.... The grievances touched on medical care, work conditions, censorship, diet, parole procedures and religious expression.

October 4, 1971   *The New York Times*
New York   "The Attica Revolt: Hour-By-Hour"
                         Joseph Lelyveld, Francis X. Clines,
                         Michael T. Kaufman and
                         James M. Markham

CHAPTER 1

Day One: News of Insurrection
Thursday, September 9, 1971

* * *

$\mathbf{T}$he day started off perfectly for off-duty New York State Trooper Anthony Strollo, Tony, to his family and friends. It was a clear, sunny September morning as Tony washed and waxed the family station wagon parked in the driveway to the modest two-family house where he lived with Marie, his wife of six years and their two sons Anthony Jr. (A.J.)* age 4, and Michael* age 2. Tony's Aunt Alice* and Uncle Bill* resided in the other half of the duplex located in upstate Batavia, New York.

Inside the house, Marie was busy tending to the two boys while listening to the local radio station. She patted each child on the head before they ran out the front door to play. Marie watched them for a moment then flipped the dish towel over her right shoulder as she headed toward the kitchen and a sink full of breakfast dishes.

Outside, A.J. and Michael ran down the front steps and chased each other around where Tony was working. Slipping in the puddles of water, they headed back toward the house laughing and giggling. Tony glanced up and chuckled as he hosed down the sudsy car.

"Boys!" he called out. "Don't track any water into the house

7

or Mommy will not be happy," he advised as he watched his sons disappear back inside the house.

Hearing the front door slam, Marie paused long enough to walk into the adjoining dining room to look out at the boys in the living room which had toys and books scattered about.

"Why don't you boys settle down now and put some of those toys away?"

"But, Mom, you promised to read us a story," A.J. reminded her.

"And I will," promised Marie as she dried her hands off on the towel that lay across her shoulder. "Just as soon as your toys are picked up."

A.J. ruffled his little brother's hair before doing as his mother had requested. Mimicking his older brother, Michael bent down and tried to gather several toys at once, managing to drop them all. Marie smiled warmly as she watched her children for a moment before returning to the kitchen to finish drying the dishes. But the local radio newscast caught her attention.

"...there are unconfirmed reports that hostages have been taken. We will keep you informed as more news is received. Now back to our regular program."

Marie stiffened in front of the sink as chills raced down her spine. Her eyes darted toward the radio which was now playing music. Did she hear the report correctly? Suddenly, she spun around looking for Tony, momentarily forgetting that he was outside. Throwing the dish towel back over her shoulder, Marie rushed to the front door almost tripping over her two sons who were once again playing with their toys on the living room floor.

Marie burst through the front door catching Tony's attention. He saw the worried expression on her face.

"What is it, Marie?"

She hesitated a moment. "Tony. A report just came over the radio." She paused a moment to catch her breath. She really did not want to repeat the news. She hoped that maybe it was not true, or that she had heard it wrong. "There is an insurrection at Attica Prison. I..." Marie swallowed hard, staring at her husband. "I wonder if your brother is working?"

Tony's face took on a serious expression as his mind raced ahead. "Call Frank's wife and ask her if Frank is working," he advised her as he quickly packed up his cleaning tools, bucket and hose.

Marie nodded absently as she dashed back inside the house to phone her sister-in-law. Marie felt as though she was manuevering through a dream...or a nightmare. She prayed it wasn't the latter.

Marie was not an alarmist by nature. Actually, she was quite level-headed and well-educated. At 26, she was a very attractive brunette who kept in shape by chasing after her two boys. Marie loved being a mother and a housewife. There were times though, when being a cop's wife was definitely difficult and she knew there was not a woman out there who was married to one who did not share her point of view. It took a certain type of person to understand the emotions and moods that went with being married to a cop. It was a great responsibility in itself. One had to be a bit more patient, a bit more understanding, a bit more empathetic and totally capable of giving comfort and love when needed. Being married to Tony was wonderful. She had a happy life and could not have picked a better husband. Tony was a complete professional in everything that he chose to do. Marie always felt proud of him and she had the highest confidence in his abilities not only as a Trooper, husband and father; but as a human being as well.

Marie knew that her husband was doing what he wanted to do - he was a New York State Trooper - and she sought solace in the fact that he was fortunate enough to be able to work at a job in a career that he loved. It was still hard for her at times, however. There was always the constant unspoken worry of whether or not he would arrive home safely after his shift. That was always there, like a permanent fixture. But Marie's confidence in Tony's ability and training was unshakeable. She knew Tony would and could take care of himself in any situation. Even when he was a Correctional Officer (C.O.) at Attica Prison, Marie knew he would be okay, even though it was not exactly the career choice of his dreams. When Tony joined the State Police, Marie didn't know who was more pleased - Tony or her.

Life seemed very calm and sedate for the Strollos. Marie was content with her duties and responsibilities on the homefront as well as being a part-time nurse at a nearby hospital, and Tony was more than happy being a member of the New York State Police.

Please, God. Don't let things change now, prayed Marie as she reached for the kitchen wall phone, kicking away the small beige step stool that she always left there so A.J. could reach the phone. Right at that moment, Marie felt as though she was moving in surreal motion. Her mind was racing ahead thinking about what might possibly be going on over at Attica. Thinking of friends and relatives working there in possible danger...while her sensible side was straining to remain calm.

Outside, Tony packed up his wax and rolled away the hose. He knew if there was an insurrection over at the prison, things had to be pretty intense. He prayed to God that his brother was not at work.

Inside the house, Marie hung up the phone with a heavy sigh as she briefly squeezed her eyes shut to hold off a rush of tears. She met Tony at the front door. Their eyes met.

"Well?" asked Tony.

"Your brother *is* working, Tony."

Tony glanced away a moment, his jaw muscle flexing. "I'll probably be recalled to duty."

Almost simultaneously, the telephone rang. A.J. rushed into the kitchen to grab for it, Marie at his heels.

"I got it, Mommy," called A.J. as he slid the stool under the phone.

"No!" Marie yelled sharply, catching her son by surprise. She noted the confusion in his tiny face and softened her tone for his sake.

"I'll get it, A.J. It's probably an important work call for Daddy."

Pouting, A.J. shuffled his way back through the rooms to where his brother was waiting for him.

Marie grabbed the receiver and drew in a deep breath before speaking. "Hello?"

A pause.

"He's right here, Cal. I'll let you talk to him." Marie handed Tony the receiver; worry filled her eyes. "It's your station commander, Tony."

Tony quickly took the phone. "Hello."

A long pause.

"Yes Sir, Sarge. We just heard about the situation. My brother Frank *is* working this shift at the prison, but...." Tony swallowed hard before continuing. "I don't know if he is a hostage." Tony nodded as he listened. "I'm on my way, Sarge. I'll be there shortly."

After Tony hung up the phone, he hustled off into the bedroom and proceeded to throw a few personal items into a small duffel bag and then briskly walked toward the front door with Marie right behind him.

"Well?" Marie asked, a nervous edge to her usually calm voice.

Tony turned and held his wife close for a long moment. He pulled back just a bit to look into her dark brown eyes. "Marie, I've got to get to Geneseo now." His tone was very serious, yet he tried to be gentle with his wife.

11

Marie wanted to be strong for her husband, but found it extremely difficult to do so as she began to tremble while bravely fighting back the tears that attempted to fall.

"You be careful, Tony." She turned to their two sons. "Come on, boys. Give Daddy a kiss good-bye. He has to go to work now."

A.J. and Michael jumped up and hugged their Daddy. They were all smiles. To them, it was just another day of Daddy going to work.

Tony bent down and scooped up both kids. Giving them each a kiss, he said, "You boys be good for Mommy. Daddy loves you both and will see you later." Tony placed the children back down on the floor and glanced over at his wife. His brown eyes filled with emotion. "I love you too, Marie." He then leaned over and kissed Marie before heading out the door. "I don't know how long I'll be gone," he called over his shoulder.

Marie and the boys rushed over to the front door and watched as Tony jumped into the station wagon. "Keep in touch, Tony," she called over the revving of the car's engine. "Let me know as soon as you find out anything about Frank."

Tony nodded as he pulled the car door shut.

"I love you, Tony!"

Marie hugged her two sons tightly as she watched Tony's car squeal off down the street. She tried to shake the feeling of uncertainty that was spreading through her.

* * *

Enroute to Geneseo, Tony passed traffic on Route 63. With his car lights on, he blew past a local highway crew working on a section of road. Seeing his fast moving car, the workers quickly jumped out of Tony's way. Tony knew if the traffic remained light, he could easily make the 25-mile trip to the station in under 20 minutes in the family wagon.

Driving along, his thoughts came in jumbles. He didn't even know how he was supposed to feel. He couldn't keep from wondering how his brother was, or if Frank was still alive. His brother worked in the prison commissary, but was he there now? Was he safe? The one thing Tony knew his brother had in his favor was that Frank was generally well-liked at the prison. And that was a definite plus at a time like this.

Other thoughts dodged in and out of his mind. Fond memories of times spent with Frank as children came flooding back to Tony. As well as times they spent at Attica as fellow Correctional Officers.

Tony recalled the day he had been granted a six-month leave of absence by the Warden so he could attend the State Police Academy. It didn't seem like three years had passed since that day.

Tony, dressed in his C.O. uniform, had stood before the Warden of Attica.

"So, you want to be a Trooper, huh?" asked the Warden.

"Yes Sir, Warden," responded Tony.

"I will give you a six-month leave of absence. If you feel you need an additional six months, you can write and ask for an extension. Understood?"

"Yes, Sir"'

"Good luck," the Warden added.

"Thank you, Sir." Tony saluted, then left the Warden's office a very happy man.

Tony slipped on his sunglasses as he drove along Route 63. A slight grin crossed his lips. He knew he would never return to Attica as a C.O. No way. He knew the only way he'd be back was as a Trooper. His grin faded. Now here it was, three years later, and Tony was doing exactly that. He wondered what in the hell had gone wrong over there? Tony reached around and rubbed at the back of his neck. He'd soon find out what was going down, he thought grimly as he tightened his grip on the steering wheel.

* * *

"The waiting is the worst part," Marie said in between sips of coffee.

Sitting across the kitchen table from her was Tony's Aunt Alice, who lived next door. Alice was a warm, slightly overweight woman in her mid-fifties. Studying Marie a brief moment, she slipped a stray gray hair behind her ear before reaching across the table to pat Marie's hand. "As soon as Tony knows something, I'm sure he'll call," Alice said in a gentle voice trying to reassure Marie.

Marie nodded as she glanced over at the radio on the dining room buffet. It hadn't been turned off since she first heard of the insurrection. Little did she know that the radio would soon become her lifeline to Tony and Frank. "I know, Aunt Alice. I keep listening to that radio," she said nodding toward it. "But there's nothing new." Marie sighed as she looked at Tony's aunt. "I guess they don't know anything yet."

Alice glanced around for the boys. She pushed herself out of the chair and walked into the dining room to get a view of the boys playing with some toys on the living room sofa while watching cartoons on the television set. Alice smiled then headed back into the kitchen and poured more coffee. After replacing the percolator back on the counter, Alice sat down and watched Marie absently dump spoonfuls of sugar into her coffee mug. Alice grimaced then reached over and covered the sugar bowl.

"The boys seem to be taking it in stride."

Marie stared into her cup. "I'm glad they're too young to understand. A.J. thinks Daddy went to work just like every other

14

day. And naturally I'm not going to say anything about their Uncle Frank."

Alice sipped the hot brew. "I'm sure everything will be just fine, Marie."

Marie looked over at Alice with an uncertain expression. "Oh, Aunt Alice," she sighed while trying to brave a false smile. "How I wish I could believe that." Marie pinched her eyes shut in an attempt to stop the flow of tears.

Alice slid her chair around the table, situating herself directly next to Marie. "Marie, what is it?" she asked as she slipped an arm around Marie's shoulders.

Marie traced her mug with a shaky finger while chewing on her lower lip. Her voice was low, her thoughts obviously far away. "A few months ago, I had this terrible dream. I even told Tony about it." Marie glanced at Alice while wiping away the moistness under her eyes. "What if it comes true like the others?"

Alice remained her usual calm self. "Why don't you tell me about this one, Marie? Did it have something to do with Tony? Is that why you're so upset now?" Alice shrugged. "Maybe I can help you to...decipher it?"

Marie closed her eyes and leaned back in the chair. "I can't say it was a dream...it was more like a nightmare...." Marie could feel the terror race through her very being as she began to recall the dream. She could almost hear the steady, choppy whir of the helicopter blades cutting the air. Her body began to tremble as she once again felt a sense of fear spread through her body from the memories of the horrible dream that have haunted her ever since, night after night.

"Marie." Alice gently shook Marie's arm as Marie's eyes remained fixed on some unseen thing in the distance.

"Marie!" Alice called again, finally drawing Marie's attention back to the present.

Marie stared blankly at Alice, almost as though she saw right through the woman. Her voice was a mere whisper. "I remember feeling so...scared. Especially when...," Marie's voice trailed off with the memory.

Alice waited for Marie's unfinished words. "Especially when *what*?"

Marie blinked several times, focusing her eyes on Aunt Alice. She sighed deeply. "I saw Tony there. I saw him in the midst of all this terrible chaos and confusion. He climbed up what I think was some type of ...I don't know, a...ladder?"

Alice rubbed Marie's arm before standing up to clear the table. "Marie, honey. I know how unsettling your dreams are to you. But please keep in mind it was just that, a bad dream."

Marie absently nodded.

Alice continued on. "Not *all* of your dreams have been bad. And not every one has come true." Alice placed the dirty cups and spoons into the sink. "Besides, it probably has nothing to do with what's happening over at the prison." Alice turned and studied Marie a brief moment before adding in a weak voice, "Right?"

Marie raised an eyebrow in Alice's direction.

As Alice returned to her seat, little Michael came shuffling into the kitchen and laid his head on Marie's lap.

"Tired, sweetie? Why don't you go take a nap on the couch?" Marie smiled at her son as she rubbed his blond hair. Marie waited until after he left the room before speaking again. "Oh, Aunt Alice. I'm not just worried about Frank anymore. Not after that dream. I'm really worried about Tony, too." Tears slipped down Marie's cheek. It wasn't like her to cry. But the dream had left her visibly upset.

A.J. rushed into the room, with Michael chasing after him. Alice watched as A.J. kept teasing his brother. "Would you like me to take the boys next door for a couple of days?" she offered.

Marie shook her head. "No, thanks. My brother is going to drive over and stay with us for the weekend."

Alice smiled. "That's good. How is Joseph's training going? Do you think he'll like being a Buffalo cop?"

"Yes. He seems to like being a cadet, but I think he'll be glad to finish," she said, smiling briefly as she watched the two boys run back toward the living room. "So much for a nap."

"Well," Alice stated. "I'm glad he's coming. But if you need anything until then, you know we're right next door."

Marie rested her weary head on her hand. "Mmm-hmm."

Alice grew concerned. "Are you sure you're okay, Marie?"

Marie nodded. "I'm fine. I just hate having those dreams." Marie looked at Alice. "They usually *do* come true."

The troopers of the New York State Police were correct and outwardly unemotional - as if this were just another mission. They were very conscious of their professional reputation.

1972   *Attica-My Story*
New York   Russell G. Oswald,
                                  Commissioner of Corrections of
                                  New York State during the
                                  Attica Riot.

(A State Police) Major said he was under orders not to discuss the attack plan, but he added, "The State Police train every trooper for every kind of situation, including that (riot) situation."

1972   *Attica-My Story*
New York   Russell G. Oswald

CHAPTER 2

Reflections

* * *

While listening to a song playing on the car radio, Tony allowed his thoughts to drift back to earlier times shared with his brother, Frank.

It was 1955 and Tony had been twelve years old. He remembered wanting to run away from home because he felt he had received some non-justifiable punishment from his mother. He had been very upset. He yelled at his mother in hope of making her feel as miserable as he felt, or perhaps to possibly make her retract her given punishment.

"I'm going to run away!" Tony screamed, thinking it to be a big, major threat.

"Go ahead," his mother said, waving her hand. "Where do you think you are going to go? And just who do you think will take you in?"

Determined not to give in, Tony stuck out his chin in an act of stubborn defiance. "I'll find a place," he declared before running off to his room for a change of clothes. He dropped down to the floor in search of something under his bed. He slid out his piggy bank and grasped it tightly under his arm. Tony then rushed out of the house, slamming the front door behind him. Tony managed to get as far away from home as the corner when his big brother Frank came running down the block after him.

As Tony stubbornly waited at the corner for a bus, he felt the warm, supportive arm of his brother wrap around his shoulders.

"Come on, Anthony. You don't have enough money to make it on your own yet."

Not wanting to show a sign of weakness or the tears that stung his eyes, Tony tried to give a little resistance by shrugging Frank's arm off his shoulder as he hugged his bank even tighter. Even at twelve, Tony had a fierce independent streak outweighed only by his deep sense of family love and loyalty, even if it evaded him at that very moment.

Frank once again slid his arm around Tony. "Come on, Anthony." He gently pulled Tony back in the direction of the family's house. "Let's go home."

And together, shoulder-to-shoulder, the Strollo brothers walked home.

Let's walk that walk again, Frank. Let's go home shoulder-to-shoulder, just one more time. Tony sighed deeply as he twisted his neck from side-to-side in hope of gaining some relief from the tension he could feel knotting at the base of his skull. Tension not from driving, but from not knowing what was going on behind Attica's walls and not knowing what has happened to Frank, his "Big Brother," his protector. Tony could not keep from wondering if it was Frank who now needed the protection? And if so, could little brother Anthony provide it and save him from an unknown fate? *That is,* Tony reminded himself, *if Frank is still alive.*

The Strollo's had always been a close-knit family. They had their differences as all families do, but there was a deep, inherited family bond of love. Though often times unspoken, it existed just the same. Tony prayed that he did not have to bring them bad news when it was all over. His fingers tensed their grip on the steering wheel. *When will it be over?*

Tony arched his back in the seat of the station wagon a moment before relaxing back against the leather. A slight grin tugged at Tony's mouth as he recalled how Frank always had a way of reminding Tony that he was the older one, the one in charge - even though Frank never actually said those exact words. It was more like an unspoken understanding with them. A sort of fraternal respect for each other. They never threatened each other with any type of sibling power play, but that wasn't to say that they didn't enjoy busting each other's chops once in awhile.

Tony fondly recalled a time back in 1963 when he had just returned home from Army boot camp. His hair had been buzzed and he was dressed in fatigues as he and Frank engaged in some harmless wrestling on their parents living room floor. Their three sisters, aged eleven, thirteen and fourteen, looked on in amusement. Marie, who was Tony's girlfriend at the time, frowned as she couldn't tell whether the two brothers were serious or just fooling around.

"Your brothers are crazy!" Marie said to the Strollo sisters who just shrugged and giggled. They were used to their brothers horseplaying.

Tony pushed himself up off the floor and extended a well-muscled arm out to Frank. His brother grabbed Tony's arm and hoisted himself up. Once in a standing position, Frank then turned and pushed Tony in jest.

"So you think you're a tough guy now, huh?" Frank gave Tony a mock-punch to the shoulder. "Big brother doesn't have to stick up for you anymore, huh?" he taunted.

Tony, eager to show his stuff, spun around and quickly placed his brother in a headlock. "That's right!" Tony chuckled, then brought Frank back down to the floor in one swift and easy move.

They both stared at each other a long moment before busting out in laughter.

"I guess the Army trained you well!" exclaimed Frank.

Five years later, Tony found himself standing side-by-side with Frank as fellow Correctional Officers at Attica Prison. They worked the same shift and would sometimes talk after line-up. One particular day before heading out to their separate posts, Tony walked along with Frank.

"I spoke to the Warden today, Frank. I was granted the six-month leave of absence."

"So you're going to go ahead with the State Police Academy, huh?"

Tony nodded. "Yes, I am." He glanced around their environment, shaking his head in disgust. Behind them a gate clanged shut as distant shouting voices echoed through the prison. "And I can't wait."

Frank shook his head. "You'll transfer all over the state, Anthony."

They stopped and studied each other a moment.

"It's all part of moving through life, Frank." Tony grinned. "You didn't think my joining the Army was such a good idea either, remember?" Frank returned the grin as Tony continued. "I like to keep moving on, Frank." Tony wriggled his shoulders as he darted a look around his surroundings. "Besides, I won't miss this place. The only way I'll ever come back is as a trooper."

Frank reached over and patted Tony on the back. "Then all that's left to say is good luck, Brother."

Approaching the Geneseo State Police barracks, Tony saw a definite show of force growing around the station. There were at least forty troopers and 25 black and white troop cars all over the parking lot. Tony pulled his car in behind the station and rushed through the rear entrance to the locker room where he changed into his uniform in front of his locker. The Station Sergeant entered the room.

"Report to the Lieutenant as soon as you are ready to go," he stated.

"Yes, Sir," replied Tony as he finished putting on his collar brass. Tony adjusted his black leather gun belt with one hand while holding his gray Stetson hat in the other. He quickly made his way through the long hall of the station. He paused outside the Sergeant's office as another trooper exited.

"Is Lieutenant Arthur* in there?" asked Tony as he pointed toward the office.

The other trooper shook his head negatively. "He's out front."

As Tony turned to leave, the trooper added, "Hey, I heard that your brother may still be inside Attica. Good luck, man."

"Thanks." Tony paused a moment to watch his co-worker walk down the corridor. One thing Tony felt certain of at that moment was having the support of his fellow troopers. That was the type of group they were. They watched out for each other and gave support when needed. Tony knew this was just the beginning of what was to come if Frank had indeed been taken hostage.

Lieutenant Arthur was waiting in front of the station for Tony. The Lieutenant was the Zone Commander, an ex-Marine and a man of few words who was not only strict but who also knew how to command respect from his men.

Tony stood before him. "Trooper Strollo reporting as directed, Sir."

There had been much activity going on all around them as many troopers started to line up and wait for further instructions.

"Strollo," Lieutenant Arthur spoke in a loud, clear voice

23

above all the surrounding activity. "I understand your brother works at Attica Prison."

"Yes, Sir."

"Is he working now?"

Tony nodded. "Yes, Sir. Before I left home I learned from his wife that Frank did go to work today. However, we did not receive any official word that he is a hostage."

"Didn't you work at Attica Prison before you joined the State Police?" the Lieutenant asked.

Tony knew Lieutenant Arthur was fully aware of the background of each and every man under his command, and the Lieutenant usually knew the answers to his questions before he asked them.

"Yes, Sir. My brother and I both worked there together until I joined the State Police in 1968," stated Tony.

"You should know the fastest route to Attica Prison then, right?" the Lieutenant inquired.

Behind them, the troopers had started to form ranks, waiting for the order to move out. There would be four troopers in each patrol unit for the twenty-five mile trip to Attica.

"Yes, Sir. I do. I would take Route 63 to Route 20, then Route 20 to 98 into Attica."

Lieutenant Arthur nodded his acknowledgment, then walked away as Tony scanned the troops lining up. He was growing extremely anxious to get to Attica.

Tony figured the troopers from Troop A Batavia would probably have the riot under control before all the other troops arrived, but he still wished he was already on his way to Attica.

Tony spotted his partners from the station and called out to them as he jogged toward them. "Don't leave without me, guys! I'll ride in your car."

These troopers, all senior men to Tony, worked well together at the Geneseo station. They often had station parties and family get-togethers. There were times, Tony reflected, upon completion of the C-line - the 3:00 p.m. to 11:00 p.m. shift - the guys would occasionally stop at a local bar to recap the tour of duty, tell "war" stories of their police experiences, and just joke around and unwind. It wasn't like "big city" police work where an officer's exposure to the criminal element of society was greater. Even though there were stations that saw more action, being on the State Police Tony believed one had a better chance of enjoying the job and rolling with the punches. In his three short years of State Police experience, the riot situation over at Attica was possibly Tony's most serious encounter.

Glancing around at the growing assembly of troops gathering outside the barracks, Tony knew not everything a trooper encountered during his career would be as unpleasant as riot situations or death. There were, of course, more pleasurable and somewhat quirky experiences as well. And for now, Tony preferred to concentrate on the lighter side of life. At least until he received some word on what was happening over at Attica.

Leaning back against a parked troop car, Tony grinned as he recalled a specific incident that certainly covered the lighter side of the job. He had been running radar on Route 63 just a couple of miles west of the station. It had been about a month ago when a sports car sped by him clocking 79 mph on the radar unit Tony had been observing. Tony pulled out and gave chase, finally stopping the compact red car just outside the Village of Geneseo. Tony stepped out from his unit and proceeded to walk up to the driver's side door with his hat and sunglasses on, his hand near his gun as a standard precaution. As he neared the sports car, he viewed a beautiful young lady in her early twenties seated behind the wheel.

"License and registration please," Tony requested in his usual determined tone of voice.

The young lady smiled up at Tony.

Looking down at her, Tony could see that the woman was clad in a skimpy bikini bathing suit.

"What's wrong, Officer?" she queried innocently.

"I stopped you for speeding. Seventy-nine miles per hour in a fifty-five mile per hour zone," he stated matter-of-factly. "Your license and registration please," he repeated.

"Officer, can't you just give me a warning this time?" she asked, still smiling sweetly at Tony as she continued to offer him full view of her scantily clad body.

"I am sorry, Miss. Maybe the judge could give you a warning. I only enforce the law," Tony replied as he held out his hand for the requested identification.

"Okay," the woman sighed as she reached across the seat to retrieve her paper work. She handed the information out the window to Tony. "Here's my license and registration, Officer. I know you got to get your quota," she added with a smile.

Tony wrote the woman a ticket and sent her on her way.

Later that night, after his shift, Tony and a couple of the guys stopped at a local tavern for a beer. To Tony's surprise, he heard a familiar female voice.

"There's the trooper who gave me a ticket today," she announced loudly as she walked over to Tony with several of her friends. "Hello," she said to Tony.

Tony nodded his greeting. At least this time she was fully clothed.

"Say," the young lady drawled as she moved closer to Tony at the bar. "I *never* thought you would give me a ticket," she said, her mouth forming a wide smile. "Especially after seeing what I had on."

Tony grinned before taking a swig of his beer. More like after seeing what *little* she had on, he mused.

The girl continued on. "I am very proud of the gray uniform," she declared. "You guys are tough." She glanced over at

26

her friends who were all smiling and laughing. She turned back to Tony and spoke in a more serious tone. "I'm actually dating a trooper from your station. I told him how I put you through the test today," she admitted teasingly. "I know it cost me a ticket and risked three points on my license, but it is my first ticket and I am sure the judge will go easy on me," she said as her face broke into a broad smile. She pointed to Tony's beer. "Let me buy you a drink for doing your job!"

It's all part of the job, Tony mused as a smile crossed his lips briefly before the loud sound of a car door slamming snapped his attention back to the present situation. He glanced around at his fellow troopers readying themselves for whatever waited ahead for them. This will be a difficult situation, thought Tony, especially if the inmates harm any of the guards or take hostages.

Looking around at his colleagues, all of them armed and ready to do what they must at only a moment's notice, Tony realized now why the drill instructors at the academy had been so strict, especially when it came to the use of weapons.

There had been an incident at the academy, Tony recalled, that led one recruit to quit. The class had gathered back at the barracks, after a long day at the shooting range.

"If you don't have it in you to kill another human being who is about to kill you or another innocent person," shouted one lead drill instructor as he looked around the room filled with recruits. "Then you might as well quit the job now."

Tony glanced around the room. He could see that one particular recruit was having trouble with what the drill instructor had to say. Tony noted a pained expression on the guy's face.

Apparently the drill instructor noticed it too. "You got a problem with that, Trooper Harvy*?" shouted the instructor as he confronted the recruit.

"Yes, Sir. I think I do," responded the recruit.

"What is it?" yelled the instructor.

"Sir, I don't think I could ever kill another person," Harvy replied. "Even if my life was in danger."

Tony stared at the other man. He couldn't believe what he had just heard. How could someone feel that way, say it, and still want to be a trooper?

The drill instructor also appeared to be in a state of disbelief. He looked about the room at all the other recruits. "How does the rest of the class feel about that?" The instructor saved his opinion and dropped the ball into the laps of his students.

Tony wanted to put that guy to the test. He needed to see if recruit Trooper Harvy was serious. So Tony raised his hand.

"Strollo." The instructor acknowledged him.

Tony shifted in his seat to face the fellow recruit. "If a bad guy was going to kill you or your wife, wouldn't you try to kill him first if you had the chance?" Tony asked, knowing that had to get through to the guy. If it was Tony or Marie or the boys who were being threatened, Tony had not a doubt about what action he would take. He would defend his family and his own life right to the bitter end.

"No," Trooper Harvy replied quietly. "I could never take another person's life."

Tony stared at the man in total disbelief. *What in the hell are you doing here, you jackass?* Tony's mind screamed. He wanted to jump up and shake some sense into Harvy. Tony heard the groans and laughs of his fellow classmates who were just as stunned at Harvy's answer. Tony was thankful he wasn't related to the guy and he certainly would never want to have him as back-up. He'd be the type of guy to sacrifice his partner's life before he would even think to draw his gun in self-defense.

"See me in my office after supper, Trooper Harvy," the drill instructor directed the recruit in a deadly serious voice.

The next day, recruit Trooper Harvy was history. Word had it that he resigned after the drill instructor enlightened him on how his negligent actions could cost another person their life.

A guy like Harvy we do not need on this detail, thought Tony as he watched the other troopers mentally prepare themselves for the situation at Attica. *Thank God the academy knows how to screen recruits that can't make it before they graduate. I wouldn't want to go into Attica with another Trooper Harvy next to me. I might never come out alive.*

Not far from the prison, a Corrections officer told a reporter from the New York DAILY NEWS that almost everybody in Attica resented the press:

"They feel that all the reporters did their best to make the Corrections Officers look bad and the prisoners look good. People don't take into account that some of the men in that prison really are bad men. The way things are nowadays, people don't get sent to prison right away. To be sent to prison these days, you have to be bad and some of these men are bad. Bad people."

1972   *Attica-My Story*
Doubleday & Co., Inc.   Russell G. Oswald

CHAPTER 3

The Preparation

* * *

"Listen up!" directed the commanding voice of Lieutenant Arthur to the formation of fifty or more troopers. "I want you troopers to mount up in troop cars with four troopers per car...we don't want to take unnecessary cars." Lieutenant Arthur glanced around at his men before continuing. "The first troop car reaching main intersections as we proceed down Route 63 to Route 20, and Route 20 west to Attica, will drop off and stop traffic for the entire convoy of troop cars. When the last car passes, that troop car will fall-in to the rear of the convoy and the next first troop car will take the next main intersection, and so on." Lieutenant Arthur slowly walked around checking out the formation. "Once we start this convoy, we don't want to stop until we get to Attica. We just got word that things are getting worse there." The Lieutenant stopped to study his men. "Any questions?"

"Yes, Sir," a trooper responded. "What will our assignment be once we arrive at Attica?"

"The Troop Commander of Troop A Batavia is in charge at this point and we will get our assignment from that chain of command once we arrive," stated Lieutenant Arthur. "Any other questions?"

A silence.

"If not, let's mount up and move out!" he directed with determination.

Tony felt his adrenaline kick in as he jumped into a troop car operated by one of the senior troopers from the station. "Are we ready, Bob*?"

"Yeah," Bob replied. "We'll take the lead and be the first troop car to block the intersection of Route 36 and 63 in Greigsville."

"Sounds good," Tony responded as he looked out the passenger window, his thoughts on his brother. *Please, Frank, be alive. I'll be there soon.*

Two other troopers slid into the back seat and Bob maneuvered the car into the lead position of the convoy. Within minutes, they were at the intersection of Routes 36 and 63 in Greigsville. Situated on one corner was a gas station where many of the locals hung out. It was obvious to Tony that the people had heard the news about the insurrection because they were standing by the roadside waving as the convoy approached the intersection. The troopers always received excellent support from the community. The town did not have their own local police department, so they depended on the State Police as their only means of protection and law enforcement.

Today, however, was different than the usual day. There would be no stopping to speak with townspeople or the local gas station owner. No current events to speak of. No community news to chat about. That would all have to wait for another day. The only news anyone was concerned with at that moment was what was going on over at Attica.

As Bob stopped the unit, Tony slid out and blocked the north side of the intersection and Trooper Ben Davis* slid out from

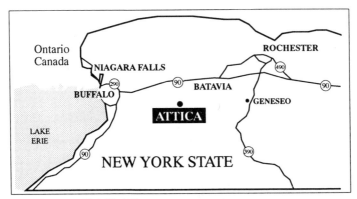

Map of western New York State

the rear seat to block the south side of the intersection. The convoy moved at a steady speed of about 80 miles per hour, bumper-to-bumper past Tony. When the last troop car passed, Tony and Ben jumped back into their unit and rejoined the procession. They soon approached the intersection of Route 63 and 20, an area commonly referred to as "Texaco Town" because it mainly consisted of a diner at one corner and a Texaco gas station on the other. The convoy made a left turn at the intersection and proceeded onto Route 20, continuing westbound to Attica Prison, twenty minutes away.

Upon arriving at the prison, a detail of Troop A members was already in place awaiting further instructions. Word had it that several hostages were being held by the rebel inmates, but the hostages names had not been confirmed. Troopers continued to flow into the area from all parts of the state. The Troop E detail from Geneseo parked, then gathered in an area just outside the front prison walls where they waited pending further instructions.

Tony recognized many of the C.O.s from when he was one during his stint at Attica. Trying to assess the situation, Tony walked over to Guard Post Tower 13 which was located left of

33

the prison's main entrance - standing atop of the thirty foot concrete walls. Looking up at the tower, Tony used his hand to shield
his eyes from the bright sun. The guard from inside walked out
onto the observation deck to glance down at Tony.

"How is it going up there?" asked Tony.

"Is that you, the former Corrections Officer Tony Strollo
who went on to better things and joined the State Police
some...three years ago?"

Tony grinned. "You got that right!" Tony exclaimed. "How
is my brother, Frank, doing?" he asked in a more serious tone.

"Frank is still inside the institution. We don't know if he is
hiding or if they have taken him hostage," the guard spoke apolo-
getically.

"Okay, thanks," Tony replied, wishing the news could have
been better. "Let me know if you find out anything about him."

"Sure thing," replied the guard. "Nice to see you again...good
luck," he added before disappearing back inside the tower.

By late afternoon, they still did not know how many

New York State Police arrive at Attica   *Photograph courtesy of Anthony R. Strollo*

New York State Police arrive at Attica

photographs courtesy of Anthony R. Strollo

hostages had been taken by the inmates. And Tony did not have a clue as to whether his brother was dead or alive.

The wait seemed to last forever to Tony and his fellow troopers who were gathered around the exterior of the prison. As more troops arrived, they exited their units clad in riot helmets and holding gas masks as they mustered around.

As the troopers organized, a State Police BCI Captain addressed them in a very stern voice:

"...your instructions are that your weapon is not to be taken or you to be taken. You'll be sent in groups of five-man teams and you'll operate as a five-man unit. You're to meet force with force. There have been some of the prison personnel severely injured here this morning, and we certainly don't want to see any of our people hurt."

Tony now knew from the captain's words that things had indeed taken a very serious turn. *"There have been some of the prison personnel severely injured here this morning."* The captain's words haunted Tony. He hoped that one of the injured wasn't Frank. And he prayed that his brother and the other hostages were still alive. The worse part was not knowing. And

Police Briefing   *Photograph courtesy of Anthony R. Strollo*

Attica Correctional Facility   *Photograph by Thomas A. Strollo*

Attica Correctional Facility
Photograph by Thomas A. Strollo

Attica Correctional Facility
Photograph by Thomas A. Strollo

no one knew just how long the wait was to be.

Later that evening, Tony strolled through the growing mass of troops. The sky was pitch dark as a huge glow seemed to rise from within the prison walls, stretching out from behind the massive concrete and brick structure. Tony followed the wall up to the top as his eyes scanned the length of it as the tower lights illuminated the exterior. It was an eerie aura that surrounded the facility, encompassing all in its immediate area. For all the time Tony spent as a C.O. at Attica, the prison never affected him the way it had now. It was a cold, formidable presence that separated good and evil; only now it seemed the evil had gained the upper hand. It served as a separation between Tony and his brother; a separation of hostages and families. A silent, unyielding cold presence that Tony knew they all would have to contend with - sooner or later.

What in the hell is going on in there? Tony turned his attention back to his fellow troopers. He wondered just how long they all had to wait to receive some word - any word - on what was going on. Confusion was definitely in the air. Confusion mingled with concern for those trapped by the rebelling inmates on the other side of the wall.

And Tony still did not know how or where his brother was.

* * *

Marie gazed off into the night through the screen door as the loud chirping of crickets filled the air. Her thoughts were miles away with her husband and brother-in-law. In the background, both the television and the radio played as though embroiled in a duel for attention, though neither media drew Marie's attention for the moment. She never turned off either one just in case there was a news update. At that point, the media served as an umbilical cord to her husband. It was her lifeline.

The media was the only means of following the unfolding events at Attica until she heard from her husband. *If I hear from him.* Marie forced the fear back down deep inside herself. She would not allow it to take over. It was way too early in the lousy game to allow her emotions to go astray. She needed to be strong not only for herself, but for her children and Tony as well. They certainly did not need her to be strung out with worry. Besides, everything may turn out just fine, she tried to convince herself without much success.

Turning away from the screen, Marie closed the front door and leaned against it for a moment as if to gather strength. Absently, she stared at the television set.

No new news.

Slowly, she ascended the stairs and opened one of the bedroom doors. Peering in, she smiled as she watched her two sons sleeping so peacefully in their beds as a slight glow from a nearby nightlight reflected off their golden hair. *The innocence of youth.* Marie quietly closed the door to their room. She crossed the hall to the master bedroom where yet another television played giving a no-news update of the riot. Her eyes riveted to the set, Marie sat down on the edge of her bed. After the update, Marie focused on a crucifix that hung on the wall above her dresser. Closing her eyes, she offered a silent prayer for her husband and his brother.

* * *

The wait seemed forever. Finally, at about ten o'clock that night, Marvin*, a close friend and former co-worker of Tony's from his days as a C.O. at Attica, motioned for Tony to step away from his State Police associates and join him off to the side. It was obvious Martin wished to speak in private, which Tony knew meant only one thing - the news was not going to be good. Marvin worked close with the Warden's Office, so Tony knew he'd have the low-down on the situation inside. If there was a confirmed list of hostages, Marvin would be the first C.O. to know.

As Tony walked up to him, Marvin glanced around to ensure their privacy. "I got the official list of hostages, Tony," he said in a hushed voice. "It was confirmed that your brother Frank *is* a hostage." Marvin paused briefly, studying Tony's face. "The families have not yet been notified, so *please* do not release this information. Prison officials are making plans to notify the families of the hostages at this time. Let *them* do it Tony," he emphasized. "Please keep it to yourself. I am not supposed to be telling you this." Marvin reached out and patted his friend on the shoulder. "I'm sorry, man."

Tony thought he had been emotionally prepared for this moment. But as he stared into Marvin's sad eyes, he realized just how hard hearing the actual words hit him. *Frank was a hostage.* Fear filled every pore of Tony's body. Fear not for himself, but for Frank and the rest of his family. Fear for *all* the hostages.

Tony swallowed hard as he clasped Marvin's hand. "Thanks for the info, Marv."

After Marvin left, Tony glanced up at the thirty foot walls that surrounded the prison. He knew it now was a whole new ballgame. And Tony was well aware of the fact that his supervisors would be keeping a watch on his every move since he was so close to the situation, maybe too close. Tony knew that if he displayed anything less than complete professionalism, if he was to buckle under the pressure of having to deal with his brother being a hostage, his superiors would pull him from the detail. And that Tony would never allow to happen. He knew he could handle it. He had to not only for himself and his fellow troopers, but for his brother whose life could very well be depending on him. Not to mention his parents, especially his mother, who had not one but *two* sons involved in a riot. And he knew she feared for them both.

Tony turned and walked toward his co-workers. His mind drifted across the miles to where he knew his wife sat in fear for his and Frank's safety. And there were their sons - A.J. and Michael - who, thank God, were both home safely sleeping in their own beds miles away from the horrible unfolding situation at hand. But above all, Tony needed to keep himself in control, not to let his emotions stand in the way. It was now his turn to help his brother.

Yes, he told himself again, it was indeed a whole new ballgame. So many people were depending on him.

The end of the first long day was drawing to a close. Shortly after learning of his brother's situation, the Troop E detail at the prison was relieved by the next shift. The Zone Commander, Lieutenant Arthur, gave instructions for Tony's detail to check in at the Holiday Inn in Batavia where rooms had been reserved for the troopers. The men were then dismissed and reminded to meet out in front of the hotel at 5:30 a.m. the next morning for roll call.

As Tony got ready to leave the prison grounds, the Lieutenant pulled him aside. "Tony, you can go home for the night since you live just a few blocks from the Holiday Inn." The Lieutenant continued. "Just meet us for the 5:30 a.m. roll call."

"No thanks, Lieutenant," replied Tony. "I'd rather be with the detail just in case we're called out during the night."

"Okay, whatever you feel comfortable with. But you do have my permission to go home for the night if you like."

"See you in the a.m., Lieutenant." Tony slid into the troop car for the short ten-minute ride to the Batavia Holiday Inn. As he passed through the hotel doors into the Main Lobby, Tony mused how much the place had come to look like a State Police headquarters with all the troopers arriving and checking in at

Hostage Frank Strollo being interviewed before the rescue

Frank Strollo while being held hostage

Photographs courtesy of Anthony R. Strollo

the front desk. Tony received his key from the desk clerk. He was assigned to a room with a Trooper Jones* from the Geneseo station. It had been a long day, and 5:30 a.m. would be an early start. But once they entered their room, they both wanted to listen to the news on the T.V.

Jones flicked on the set as they tossed their gear down onto a nearby chair. Tony dropped down on one of the twin beds and closed his eyes. Jones sat down on the edge of his bed, the one nearest to the T.V. As he flipped through the channels, coverage of the riot situation was on almost every channel.

"Hey!" called Jones as he pointed to the television. "That looks like your brother."

Tony opened his eyes to stare at his brother's face on the T.V. screen. *Frank!* Tony bolted up off the bed. Frank was being interviewed by one of the reporters who had been permitted inside the prison earlier that day. A clear picture of Frank was on the screen showing his hands bound in front of him with strips of cloth as he spoke.

"Have you been treated all right?" asked the interviewer.

"Yes, I have so far," replied Frank in an emotionless tone. "Been treated very good."

"Bullshit!" Tony yelled at the screen before turning to reach for the telephone. He quickly dialed a number, then watched the broadcast as a chill crawled up his spine at the sight of his brother being held hostage and saying words Tony knew the inmates were forcing him to say.

Tony spoke into the phone, his eyes never leaving the set. "Marie, it's me. Do you have the television on?"

Back at the house, Marie watched the same interview on the bedroom T.V. as she sat on the corner of the bed talking to Tony on the phone.

"Yes, I'm watching it now," Marie answered, her voice quivering.

The T.V. interviewer continued his questioning: *"No com-*

43

plaints? No problems?"

"So far...been treated very good," responded Frank.

Tony clenched his teeth as he heard his brother say the prepared words for all of America to hear. "They're making him say that shit," he angrily told his wife over the phone.

"Tony, your family has been notified of Frank's situation," Marie advised.

Tony shook his head as his brother's image was replaced by others on the screen. He turned away feeling totally disgusted and extremely angry. "I don't want to talk to my mother or my sister-in-law on the phone, Marie. I can't tell them any more than they already know." Tony dropped down onto the bed. "Just tell them that I'm okay and Frank's okay...." A long pause. "And tell them not to worry."

"Be careful," Marie's voice sounded over the receiver. "Call me when you get a chance." Tony heard his wife's voice crack. He knew she was fighting back tears. But there was nothing he could say to comfort her.

"I love you, Tony."

Tony swallowed hard. "I love you too, Hon." He dropped the receiver back onto the phone before falling back against the softness of the bed. Tony was totally exhausted, yet he could not erase the vision of his brother from the television broadcast. Frank, his big brother, had been bound and taken hostage.

Tony had to get him out. He would not allow his brother to be killed.

As Tony slipped into an uneasy sleep, the first long day finally drew to a close.

Friday, September 10, 1971, while the leaders concentrated on shoring up the organizational structure they had improvised, other inmates in the yard were free to wander. Some filled pillowcases with cigarettes and cakes from the looted commissary and carried them across C Yard - a no man's land - to A Block, where inmates still under control had been locked in their cells on the ground tier.

Under the gaze of armed State Troopers who had turned the cells on the upper tiers into outposts, they (inmates) passed their booty through the bars and also reported on developments in the yard.

As the hours ticked away, the resentment of the troopers and guards over the restraints that had been placed upon them became almost palpable, a force with which the Commissioner would later have to reckon. Later on he would describe himself as being "besieged" by calls by Correction Officers in other prisons and other states asking, "How much longer are you going to endanger Corrections Officers' lives?"

October 4, 1971   *The New York Times*
New York   "The Attica Revolt: Hour-By-Hour"
         Joseph Lelyveld, Francis X. Clines,
         Michael T. Kaufman and
         James M. Markham

CHAPTER 4

Day Two: The Return to Attica
Friday, September 10, 1971

* * *

The second day began early for Tony and the troops as they mustered outside the Holiday Inn for roll call at 5:30 a.m. Tony and his detail fell into formation and acknowledged their names as each one was called out by the Zone Sergeant, who Tony knew to be one very sharp trooper. Not much could slip by his attention.

"Jackson,*" called the Sergeant.

Tony had heard from some of the other guys that Jackson had stayed out all night partying and had only returned to his room a short while earlier intent on catching twenty minutes or so of shut-eye, so he wasn't surprised to hear one of Jackson's buddies cover for him.

"Here!" another trooper responded in a disguised voice .

"Here my ass. Where in the hell is Jackson this morning?" the Sergeant demanded. "Someone better go get him right now," he barked out the command.

A trooper broke formation and hustled back into the hotel to get Trooper Jackson as the Zone Sergeant continued on with roll call. Several minutes later, Jackson emerged through the front door of the Holiday Inn looking quite disheveled as he adjusted his riot helmet.

Jackson tried to inconspicuously join the ranks, but he was spotted by the Zone Sergeant.

When roll call was completed, the Sergeant looked directly at Jackson. "Jackson."

"Yes, Sir?" Jackson looked a bit nervous, knowing full well that he had screwed up big time.

"You're guarding the cars today outside the prison," stated the Sergeant.

"Yes, Sir," Jackson replied as he pinched his eyes shut a moment. Tony bit back a grin. Watching the troop cars was a real bullshit detail.

After roll call, many of the troopers approached Tony to offer their support after watching the prior evening news broadcast of Frank's interview. One fellow member patted Tony on the arm. "We'll do everything to get him out alive," he promised.

Tony nodded his head in appreciation. "Thanks."

They all got into their cars and drove over to Attica to relieve the night shift. It was only about an eleven to twelve mile drive to the prison. Upon arrival, the night shift was exiting the facility. Various assignments were handed out to the new shift and Tony's group was assigned to A-Block. After entering the Administration Building, A-Block was the first cell block in the institution. One had to pass through this block in order to gain access to the others.

From the second floor of A-Block, one could look out through the barred windows into the yard below and watch the activity going on out there. Tony saw that the inmates were most definitely in control. Some of the inmates had changed out of their garments and were parading around in guard uniforms and some even donned the chaplain's garb. Tony could also see that they were carrying all types of makeshift weapons; from clubs to homemade knives.

Hostage circle in D-Yard   *Photograph courtesy of Anthony R. Strollo*

A .270 trooper (sharpshooter) handed Tony his rifle. Tony raised the weapon to peer through the scope to detect the location of his brother and the other hostages. He scanned the area and located the hostage circle where the men were being held. Tony could see through the scope that they had been stripped of their uniforms and were dressed in inmate clothing. This was done by the rebel inmates to confuse the troopers should they be given the word to move in. They would have a difficult time deciphering who was an inmate and who was a hostage. *Those bastards!* Tony's mind screamed as he saw the blindfolded hostages, their hands tied together by what appeared to be strips of white sheets as they sat around in a circle waiting for whatever fate held in store for them.

A sudden chill shot through Tony's body as he spotted his brother slumped over, sitting cross-legged on the dirt - blindfolded and hands bound. A lump formed in Tony's throat as he lowered the rifle. He thought hearing the news was bad...but seeing Frank and the others out there, helpless...was much, much worse. It was a feeling Tony had never felt before. And he prayed to God he'd never have to feel it again. It was a nauseating feeling that spread through his entire body. A sickening fueled by anger and disgust. The picture Tony viewed in D-Yard would be imprinted in his mind forever. No matter what the final outcome would be, this scene was one he would never forget.

Tony knew he had to maintain control of his emotions. There would be no time now for him to dwell on how he felt about the situation. His brother's life and the lives of all the hostages - many of them friends and former co-workers of Tony - all depended on him and all the troopers keeping a calm head about them. They were well-trained professionals with a job to do. And that's just what they would do. Tony sucked in a deep breath and summoned up strength from deep within himself. He raised the rifle once again to peer through the scope. So many of the hostages he knew. He knew their families. Their children. Marie knew many of the wives. She sat with them during Sunday mass. She shopped with them at the town's supermarket. Some of the children played with their own boys. Tony felt only the slightest relief at seeing the hostages for he knew at least for the moment, they were still alive. But should this go down badly, how would he ever be able to face the families of the men he knew so well. How would he be able to face his own family if....

No! Tony would not allow that train of thought to penetrate his concentration. The lives of all the hostages had changed drastically from the very moment the rebelling inmates captured them. Everyone's fate had been sealed. It was just a matter of time before it would be disclosed to all. Only the highest power, God Himself, knew how it would all end. The rest of them just had to play out the crazy game the inmates had laid out before them. And Tony knew he and his fellow troopers would play it to the very best of their ability. The only thing that mattered, the driving force behind them all, was to rescue as many hostages as possible and not to allow themselves or their weapons to be captured in the process.

From what Tony could see, the inmates were clearly in control of D-Yard. A trench had been dug through the yard, along the catwalk. There were many scattered makeshift tents, small campfires, mattresses scattered about and among the entire mess were the inmates who pranced about; some wearing helmets, others with rags and pieces of clothing tied about their mouths and faces - an effort to try and conceal their identities. Others did not seem to need face coverings as they strolled the yard as though they were artists proud of a completed masterpiece. Only to the watching eyes of Tony and fellow officers, this was nothing to be proud of. The rebel inmates had destroyed part of *their* home. It was a masterpiece alright, a masterpiece of hell.

Disgusted, Tony turned and handed the .270 trooper back his weapon. He had seen all he needed to see for the time being.

The Trench dug by inmates in D-Yard   *Photograph by Roy W. Clark*

He nodded his thanks to the trooper as he turned his attention back to the window for one more look. Tony cleared his throat in an attempt to relieve some of the tension that had formed there upon seeing his brother and the other hostages at the mercy of the rebelling inmates. But Tony knew nothing would clear the anxiety from his body. Nothing but an end to the situation. A happy and safe end.

Later that day, the prison chaplain Father Browning*, was permitted to go in and speak with the hostages. Tony knew Father Browning from his days as a C.O. at Attica. After he finished speaking with the hostages, he sought out Tony. "I recognized you here before," he said as he grasped Tony's hand in his own holding onto it a long moment. "Good to see you, Tony," he said releasing his grip.

"Hello, Father."

"I was able to whisper to your brother that the State Police were here and that you were with the group standing by waiting to take over and release them."

Tony, filled with emotion and unable to speak, nodded his head in thanks and offered a brief smile to the chaplain. He watched as Father Browning, an obviously dejected man, slowly walked down A-Block and out of the prison.

Tony drew in a deep breath and turned his attention back out to the yard which he now viewed through a pair of binoculars given to him earlier by one of his co-workers. He scanned the hostage circle once again to see his brother. Just seeing him alive brought temporary relief to Tony...very temporary. For Tony knew the worst was yet to come, and that was getting Frank and all the other hostages out without any casualties or fatalities. Tony studied his brother through the binoculars. Did he show any signs of emotion? Did he seem more confident since speaking with the chaplain? It was too difficult to tell. Frank, not unlike Tony himself, wore a poker face. Nobody was going to read him. Nobody. The best emotion was no emotion at all. You never let your opponent read your feelings. Never. Tony could only guess that Frank's hopes were given a lift after hearing Father Browning advise him that the troops were waiting in the wings.

Tony lowered the binoculars as he thought about the prison chaplain. Father Browning was a mild-mannered man. He was extremely caring and a very trusting person. But Tony knew he had to be feeling a bit betrayed at this point. Especially after seeing the inmates who he tried to lead to God with his teachings and prayers desecrate the very property that was so sacred and so important to him; by burning the chapel and adorning themselves with religious garb in such a sacrilegious manner. Tony knew Father Browning quite well from his two years as a C.O. at Attica, and he knew how his friend was feeling. The emotions did not need verbalizing. They could not be verbalized. Tony could only hope that somehow some of the chaplain's preachings would replay in the minds of the inmates.

The remainder of the day continued on in much of the same manner - the waiting game - as Tony spoke with many of the guards he had worked with at Attica. Intermittently, he scanned the yard keeping abreast of all the movement as well as speaking with fellow troopers and C.O.s about some of the men who had been taken hostages and how well they knew them and their families. The overall feeling was one of mutual disgust that such a terrible fate had befallen such good men.

At one point during that second day, the Warden who was escorted by a C.O., approached Tony and extended his hand in greeting. He spoke in an uneasy manner. "How are you doing, Tony? How do you like your new job?"

Tony knew the man was recalling their meeting of three years ago when he had granted Tony his leave of absence from Attica to enter the State Police Academy. "It's good, Warden," Tony said flatly. If it had been any other time, Tony would have continued on about the benefits and fulfillment of becoming a member of the New York State Police, but under the circumstances, his heart just wasn't in it. Tony studied the Warden's face. Knowing Tony's brother was one of the men being held hostage, he was truly at a loss for words. They didn't discuss Frank. They didn't have to. Tony knew the Warden well enough to know that he was a fair man. And he didn't have to talk about Frank and the hostages for Tony to know that he was really concerned about them and the unfolding situation at hand.

"I'm glad you enjoy your job with the State Police," he offered awkwardly as he shifted his weight from one foot to the other. Glancing around the cellblock, he raised an eyebrow at Tony. "I bet you never thought you'd be back here again."

Tony narrowed his eyes as he shook his head. "No. But I kinda figured if I ever *had* to come back here again," Tony sighed and crossed his arms in front of his chest, "it would be for a riot situation." *And not as a guard.*

The Warden really did not know how to respond to Tony, so he simply patted him on the shoulder, turned and solemnly walked away. Tony watched the Warden until he left A-Block, then he turned to speak with the many troopers who passed through on their way to the other cellblocks.

Tony received such a tremendous amount of moral support from everyone during this time. *I'm being watched very closely,* Tony reminded himself. He knew the brass did not want nor need him to pull a solo rescue mission. Even though it was difficult for him to just stand by and wait, Tony would never be foolish enough to attempt such a doomed feat. He was part of a team. And no matter how difficult it was for him to watch his brother and the rest of the hostages in D-Yard, Tony would wait for his orders.

Later on that day, activities centered around how to have the inmates release the hostages. One method contemplated was to have the prison water supply cut off, another was to not have any food brought into the facility for the rioting inmates. But that upset the rebels and their leaders. The inmate negotiator sent word to the administration, "You either send us food and water in here, or the hostages won't be around."

The local community began to chip in and offer their assistance. Sandwiches were made to send in to feed the hostages - and again the inmate panel stated, "...you better send in enough for everybody because the prisoners will eat first and if anything is left over, then the hostages will eat."

Needless to say, plenty of food was brought into the facility to ensure that the hostages were fed. As the food started to roll in, the troopers were given the opportunity to be briefly relieved; enabling them to step outside of the prison where the local Lions Club members and other community groups were cooking hot dogs and hamburgers on grills set up on the prison lawns specifically for the troopers.

At one point, Tony seized the opportunity to go on a short break. He headed outside to wait in line for something to eat. The scene outside the facility was an incredible one. There were so many concerned local people there - a public outpouring of hospitality from the whole community as they manned the grills, offered pre-made sandwiches and cans of soda pop. It was such an overwhelming feeling to see so many doing whatever they could to help.

While waiting in line to be served, Tony listened to some of the surrounding conversations as he grabbed a can of pop, opened it and took a long swallow.

"...One of the inmate demands was they had to have Cramer*, that activist attorney, present at the prison...," Tony overheard one server say.

Another person piped up. "Yeah, and they also requested the Black Panther leader. Why in the hell are any of their requests being granted when they're holding hostages? They're nothing more than ruthless killers, oh, but they have a right to request things? That's bullshit, if you ask me."

Tony adjusted his riot helmet and rubbed at his weary eyes. He did not want any conversation. He just wanted some food. To Tony, it no longer mattered what either side had to say. He just wanted to go in and get the hostages out. He wanted to bring them back home alive. He wanted Frank back home alive. And he wanted peace restored at the facility.

Tony took another long swig of the cold pop. It felt so good to have the cool liquid slide down his parched throat. Suddenly, he heard a commotion coming from one of the food lines behind him. He glanced over his shoulder as one of the pro-inmate group members was trying to get served a hot dog. The server denied the man access to the food outside the prison. "We don't feed our enemies," Tony overheard the man announce.

Tony proceeded through the line and got his food and another can of pop. In his opinion, the troopers were being well-fed.

It felt good to Tony to be outside of the prison even if it was only for a brief period of time. But he still could not keep from wondering how Frank and the others were managing.

Tony spotted several C.O.s coming back from a food delivery to the prison. "How's it going?" asked Tony as he finished eating his hot dog.

"Word is the food better keep rolling in," one C.O. replied. "They'll eat first, they said, and if anything is left over then the hostages will eat." The guard glanced around the lawn at all the people cooking. "Needless to say, there is plenty of food. So, the word we got is that the hostages are being fed."

Tony felt a bit better knowing that at least the inmates weren't starving the hostages. Or so they've been told.

Before heading back inside the facility, Tony glanced around the lawns one more time. It was such an overwhelming scene.

The townspeople cooking; friends and relatives of both hostages and inmates, were keeping vigil outside the prison - some crying, others wearing pained expressions of not knowing what has happened to their loved ones. Tony's gut instinct told him that the entire situation would not be over for quite some time.

Back inside the prison, Tony met up with some of the C.O.s who were voicing their displeasure over the developments at Attica.

"Things have gotten too relaxed," one C.O. claimed angrily.

"Yeah," another agreed. "It's getting so bad that most guards aren't happy writing up an inmate. You write one up for throwing food at you through the cellblock as you're trying to take head count of the inmates in their cells. You gotta take so much fuckin' abuse from them." The C.O. shook his head as he looked around his surroundings. "I wrote up an inmate for this same type of situation. Then the next day I went before the committee where I explained my complaint of the *alleged* violation I caught going on within the institution." The guard paused to fish for a cigarette in his uniform shirt pocket. "Well, the administration not wanting to make waves, of course, sided with the damned inmates." The C.O. placed the cigarette between his lips as he struck a match and lit it, drawing in a deep, long drag. He blew the smoke out hard before continuing. "Now as a result, morale among the guards sucks." He motioned toward the Administration Building with his hand. "And *they* don't know why? They kinda dismissed the charges, so the next day that same fuckin' asshole inmate spits at me. *That's* the kind of support we get in this place."

Tony cleared his throat. He just couldn't believe how bad things had gotten since he left. "I remember when I worked here. If an officer wrote up an inmate, the officer was right."

"You're damned right, Tony. The officer wouldn't be in his right mind if he wrote up an inmate for no reason,"agreed the other guard. "He would be outnumbered and wouldn't last working another day within the institution." A pause. "Now look at things. Who's in control?...the inmates," he said in utter disgust.

Suddenly, elsewhere in A-Block, Tony and the guards overheard a loud commotion. They turned to see several inmates on the opposite side of the bars engaged in some very heavy repartee with one of the State Police .270 men. From what Tony could hear, the inmates were definitely trying to bait and torment the troopers.

"Yo, pigs!" called out one inmate in a loud, jeering voice. "Come and get us so we can all kick your mother fuckin' asses, man!" A loud surge of shouts and threats rose from several inmates behind him.

Tony heard one of the troopers respond, "Don't worry, asshole. Your time *is* coming. We *will* be coming in."

"Hey, pig," Tony overheard an inmate on the outside yell in to the trooper. "C'mon out here and I'll stick that fuckin' gun up your fuckin' white ass!"

Tony pinched his eyes shut a moment. *How much of this crap are we supposed to listen to?*

"I believe you got that wrong, asshole," the trooper rifleman responded. "I'm going to stick this gun up *your* ass and blow your fucking head off."

Tony knew how difficult it was for that trooper to keep himself restrained with the malicious verbal torment the inmates were subjecting him and the other members to. He could see the tension and anger throbbing in the other trooper's face as he fought for control of his emotions.

"Fuck you, man," jeered the inmate as he laughed and glanced around at his followers before turning back to face off with the trooper. "I had your mother, and the fuckin' bitch squealed like a pig when I stuck it to her, Mr. Po-liceman" taunted the inmate.

The trooper stepped forward as he toyed with a .270 round

between his thumb and forefinger. "This bullet's got *your* name on it, mother fucker."

Tony's attention was caught by an approaching C.O. He wore a sad expression on his face as he broke the news to the men.

"We just got word that Timmy* died. They say the inmates used his body as a battering ram as they stormed Times Square. His skull was smashed several times." The C.O. fought back tears and his voice was full of sorrow. "Oh, man. And those scumbags want amnesty?"

Tony sighed as he lowered his head. He remembered Timmy. He was a young man in his late twenties. A local kid who went to school right in the Village of Attica. Like most of the officers, he had young children and a wife at home.

The consensus among the men was the same - the rioting inmates should be held accountable for Timmy's brutal murder. The irony of the whole thing was that the number one demand of the rebel inmates was amnesty for any wrongdoings during the riot, for the riot itself, and for Timmy's murder.

But that was not acceptable to the administration nor to the State Police.

"Tony, you got out of here in time," stated one officer.

"Why don't you guys think about changing careers?" Tony inquired. "Take the State Police exam. At least you'd be out there in a society where most people aren't criminals." Tony glanced over to where the heated verbal exchange between the inmates and trooper had taken place a short while earlier. "On the outside, you have a better chance of protecting yourself if someone is going to kill you."

One C.O. nodded in agreement. "Yeah, not like poor Timmy. What chance did he have?"

Tony turned and met their sad stares. "None," he responded in a serious tone. *And now what chance does my brother and the other hostages have? The same chance as Timmy?* Tony always believed he had made the right move when he left Attica to become a trooper. Now he had proof positive that he had made the best damned decision of his career.

A while later when Tony was back to his post on the second floor of A-block, he scanned the hostage circle through the binoculars in hopes of locating Frank. This time, however, his heart skipped a beat as he could not locate his brother. He felt his pulse pound in his ears as he frantically panned the yard searching for the figure of his brother, but to no avail. *Frank, where in the hell are you?* Tony lowered the binoculars, unable to fight off a sensation of dread. He did not want to return home the bearer of bad news. The thought alone that Frank could be dead sent a shudder through his body. Tony wasn't all that certain his mother could handle the news. And then there was the job of telling Frank's wife...and their kids...how would he be able to tell them that their Daddy would never be coming home? That their Uncle Tony couldn't save him? *Please, God,* Tony prayed. *Please keep Frank alive. Keep them all alive.*

A short time later, Tony once again viewed the hostage circle through the binoculars in hopes of locating his brother. A sigh escaped Tony's body as he spotted Frank entering the circle ahead of an inmate who then shoved his brother down until he was in a sitting position on the dirt. Tony lowered his binoculars a moment as he rubbed at his weary, bloodshot eyes. At least Frank was still alive.

Six o'clock finally arrived and Tony's detail was relieved by the night shift of troopers. Exhausted and extremely tense from being on alert all day, they got into their troop cars and headed back to Batavia. Tony shared a car with a trooper named Steve*, who was also from Geneseo.

Steve, who was driving, glanced over at Tony who had rested his head against the passenger window. "Do you want to swing by your place and get a change of clothes or something, Tony?" asked Steve, knowing Tony from the station and familiar with where he resided.

"Yes, thanks," answered Tony without lifting his head off the window. Tony closed his eyes and allowed his muscles to re-lax a bit now that he was out of the prison. He listened to Steve call in on the car radio that they would be making a side trip to the Strollo residence. Tony opened his eyes and stared at the passing scenery, not really noticing any of it as he thought about the days to come. Would the riot go on for days? Would it be over tomorrow? The next day? The day after? Would they free any of the hostages? Would Frank make it out alive? Would anybody make it out alive? Tony sighed deeply. Only God knew what the outcome would be.

Steve swung the troop car down onto Tony's street and parked in front of the house. It was a quiet and warm evening as they walked inside and were greeted by Marie's younger brother, Joseph*, who had opened the front door.

"How's it going, Tony?" Joseph asked as he reached out to give his brother-in-law a quick hug and pat on the back.

Marie, startled by Tony's arrival, leaped up from the sofa scattering crayons that were sprawled on her lap from coloring with the two boys.

Tony patted Joseph on the back. "Hey, Joe. I'm glad you're here. How's the academy?" Tony inquired, genuinely interested as he welcomed the chance to discuss something other than what was going on over at Attica. It was a great pleasure to be look-ing at familiar, loving faces. It plain felt good to be home again, however brief the stay.

"Fine," Joseph replied as his face filled with concern. "How are *you?*"

"Okay." Tony simply stated, not wanting to go into detail about how he was really feeling. Tony turned to his wife as she rushed into his arms. He kissed her mouth fully. God, he had missed her. He then reached down and ruffled the hair of both his sons. A.J. and Michael smiled adoringly up at their father, oblivious to the situation at hand. Steve entered the living room and nodded his greeting to Marie and smiled at A.J. and Michael.

Marie followed Tony into the kitchen where he grabbed a brown grocery bag and tossed in two cold six-packs of beer from the refrigerator.

"We're in a hurry here," he advised Marie as he brushed by her, heading toward the bathroom.

"What are you home for?" asked Marie, still surprised and thrown a bit off guard by his sudden arrival. She was so happy to see him, yet she was afraid to ask him for too many details. Afraid she wasn't going to like the answers.

"We're just stopping by for a few things. We'll be staying over at the Holiday Inn again."

Caught up in his frenzy, Marie helped Tony pack toothpaste, deodorant, and other essentials. Their two boys joined in the human train as they followed their parents back out into the living room where Steve was waiting, leaning against the doorframe.

"Did you see Frank?" Marie asked, her mounting curiosity getting the best of her. There were questions she just had to have the answers to. "Is he okay, Tony?"

"I saw him," replied Tony checking over the contents of his bag. "Through a pair of binoculars. He seems to be okay for the time being."

"What should I tell his wife? Tony," Marie reached out and touched her husband's arm to get his full attention. "What about your Mom and Dad?"

Tony looked into Marie's frightened eyes. He wished he could put her at ease. He wanted to, but he couldn't. Not now. Not until after.... "I can't tell them anything new, Marie."

Marie picked up the living room telephone and extended the

receiver out to Tony. "I think you should at least call them. Tell them something...anything, Tony."

Michael started to tug at Tony's pant leg. He was very happy and excited to see his father. He wanted to play.

"Daddy! Daddy!" A.J. exclaimed happily as he jumped up and down trying to get his Dad's attention. "Can you give me my bath tonight? Are we going to play now? Want to see my coloring picture Mommy did with me today?" he asked in rapid succession before running over to the sofa to retrieve his artwork.

Tony took the receiver from Marie and replaced it back on the phone cradle. "Not now, Marie."

A.J. rushed back over to Tony proudly waving his picture in front of his father.

Marie sighed as she bent down and scooped Michael up into her arms as she placed her arm around A.J. "Not now, A.J. Daddy has to go back to work."

"Why?" whined A.J. "He just got home."

Tony placed his bag down a moment and hoisted up his oldest son. "Are you my big boy?" he asked as A.J. bravely nodded. "Good. Now you know how sometimes Daddy has to go to work a lot?" Tony continued on while A.J. frowned. "Well, this is one of those times," he explained in a very soft and gentle voice. "So you get ready for bed and be a good boy for Mommy. I love you guys," Tony said as he glanced from one son to the other. Tony placed A.J. back down on the floor. "Be good now, okay? I'll be home soon," Tony said as he smiled at his boys. "I promise."

Marie bit back tears. *I'm going to hold you to that*, she swore to herself.

Tony turned and kissed his wife briefly. "See you later. We've got to get over to the Holiday Inn," he told Marie. "I'll be staying with the troops just in case we get the word to move in during the night. I'll get in touch with you by phone when I can."

Steve smiled at Marie. She knew him from the station picnics they all attended.

"We'll take care of Tony for you," he offered, knowing how worried she was. "We're going to the hotel and discuss our strategy to bring this situation over at the prison to a halt."

Marie swallowed hard as she hugged Michael closer to her. She already knew the answer to her next question, but she had to ask just the same. "It's pretty bad, isn't it?"

Steve nodded grimly.

"I'll call your wife, Steve. Is there anything you want me to tell her? Do you need anything or want her to bring anything over to you?"

"I don't need anything, thanks." Steve then followed Tony out of the house and into the darkness.

Marie stared after them into the twilight of evening long after their unit had disappeared down the street. She knew Tony could take care of himself in any situation, but this was different. Marie did not know what his odds were. All she did know was that she loved him and wanted him back home safely when it was all over.

Releasing another sigh, Marie placed Michael down on the floor and watched him briefly as he toddled off to find his brother. Turning back to glance outside, Marie thought about Tony and Frank. She knew that if one of the Strollo brothers had to lose their life as a result of the riot, and she hated to admit it even to herself because of how horrible it sounded, but she knew the better choice was Tony. For Tony, it would be an honorable demise. But it wouldn't be for Frank. A sudden chill raced through her body at the direction her thoughts had taken. She rubbed her hands up and down her arms in a feeble attempt at warmth. But she knew she was right. Tony was a trooper. He was trained for this type of situation. And Marie knew, as frightening as the thought may be, if he *had* to die he would choose to do so in the line of duty fighting for what he believed in. Fighting to save the lives of others who were in danger.

But Frank, he was a different story. He was a hostage. And Marie knew in her heart that nobody should have to die in that manner.

Marie squeezed her eyes shut. She prayed that neither of them would have to sacrifice their life for Attica.

* * *

Outside of the Holiday Inn, Steve parked the troop car. As Tony and Steve stepped out of the car, they saw Lieutenant Arthur watching them. Tony knew the Lieutenant had heard Steve's radio transmission about going to the Strollo residence.

Tony walked toward the hotel door carrying his brown paper bag under his arm. He knew it was not going to go unnoticed. Tony smiled. "How are you doing, Lieutenant?" he asked in a chipper voice.

"Very good, Tony," replied Lieutenant Arthur as he fell into step alongside Tony and Steve as they approached the hotel door. "So, what do you have in that bag?" his sharp voice demanded an answer as he motioned toward the bag with a slight jerk of his head.

Tony continued to grin. "Just something cold to drink, Lieutenant. If you'd like some, just come on up to our room and we'll have one for you."

"No, thanks. I'll pass," stated the Lieutenant giving them a visual once-over. "Just be ready to go in the morning, guys," he warned them.

"Yes, Sir, Lieutenant!" replied Tony and Steve in unison. Then, accompanied by a few other trooper friends, they headed up to the room for a few cold ones.

Later that evening, Tony phoned Marie. As he sat on the edge of the bed, he nodded his head as he spoke into the receiver. "I know, you're right, Marie. I should go over and talk to Mom and Frank's wife. I'll just tell them what I know is going on over at the prison. I guess maybe I can give them some confidence...or hope... or something."

A long pause.

"Okay, hon. Yes, I'm glad your brother is there too. He can help you with the boys. It'll be good for A.J. and Michael to have him around as well."

Another pause.

"Just come pick me up as soon as you can and we'll go on over to my parents' house." Tony sighed. "Okay, Marie. See you in a bit. Bye." He hung up the phone and dropped back against his pillow. Pinching his eyes shut, he ran a hand through his mass of black hair. He was extremely tired. And somehow, the prospect of visiting with his family during this time was not exactly tempting. He really had no new news for them, and he knew they were going to have a zillion questions for him that he would not be able to answer. Tony knew it was emotionally difficult for all of them, and he knew there was nothing he could really do to ease their anxiety. He was trying hard to maintain his own emotions, yet he knew this was something he *had* to do. Marie was right. He owed them some type of news, even if in doing so would send him into an emotional hell. But if his words could bring them a little comfort, then that's what he would do.

When Marie arrived in front of the hotel with the station wagon, Tony slid in next to her. They sat in silence most of the ride to his parents' house. Marie felt herself trembling as she alternately tightened and lessened her grip on the steering wheel. At one point, she had to steer with one hand and then the other as she wiped the sweat from her palms onto her slacks. She could feel the tension lump up in her throat as her stomach tightened. If Tony hadn't been sitting next to her, she was certain she would have been sick. But she was trying desperately to put on a brave front for him. She knew he had all he could do to muster up the strength to face his family. Marie did not want to add to his turmoil. She would have plenty of time alone later to break down if she needed to. But she refused to do it in front of Tony. The last thing she wanted was for him to go back to Attica with yet another worry on his mind. There was only so much a person could take...and Marie knew her husband was dealing with much more than his fair share.

Upon arriving at his parents' house, Tony realized just how long of a night it really was going to be as he was greeted by his mother who was so distressed and upset, she was actually to the point of believing that Frank was already dead. Tony tried desperately to calm his mother down and get her to stop crying. It was beginning to become extremely difficult for Tony to keep control over his own bridled emotions as he listened to his mother's sobs.

"Ohhh, my poor son," cried Mrs. Strollo as she clung to Tony. "Oh, Anthony. My two boys are involved in this riot. One a hostage and one a trooper waiting to go in," moaned his mother as she wiped at her wet eyes with a tissue Marie handed to her. She drew in a deep breath before continuing on. Marie knew it was hard for Tony to listen to it all, but she also knew it was extremely important for his mother to discuss it. Marie knew she *needed* to talk about it to Tony.

"This is like war," cried Mrs. Strollo reaching up to embrace her son with a King Kong squeeze, though the woman was a mere five feet tall. With tears streaming down her cheeks, she looked at her son's face. "What's wrong with those prisoners? What's wrong?" She shook her head, not understanding at all. "This is like war," she repeated.

Tony saw how red and bloodshot his mother's eyes were obviously from hours of crying and worrying about her two sons. It was apparent that she had not slept for quite some time. Tony raised his head to look over at his father who stood nearby watching. He was a tall, strong man. Always in control of his emotions, not unlike his son, Tony. But he could not hide the concern and worry that were etched in his face. He listened intently to his son, waiting and hoping to hear just the right words.

Tony could not ease himself away from his mother's embrace. Abrubtly, he reached for the nearby telephone. "I need to call Frank's wife," he announced after he cleared his throat several times. He dialed a number with one hand while holding the receiver with the other. All the while his mother stood close by, holding onto her son for fear letting go might mean letting go of him forever.

Marie and Tony exchanged knowing glances. She realized just how difficult it all was for her husband and as she listened to her mother-in-law's weeping. Marie silently brushed away her own tears, wishing she could carry some of Tony's emotional burden for him. Not only did he have to carry around the responsibility of his job and the delicate and dangerous detail he was on, but he also had the added stress of having his brother held hostage pending rescue, if Frank lived that long. But to top it all off, Tony now had to bear the burden of knowing that his parents were looking to him as their only means of contact with Frank. Tony had become their lifeline to their oldest son. Marie knew they were counting on Tony to bring his brother back home alive.

Marie bit back tears as she walked over to wrap her arms around Mrs. Strollo, but her eyes never left her husband. "Mom, the troops are looking after Frank and the others. And the Correction Officers are all doing their best," Marie tried to console her mother-in-law as she gently massaged the woman's back. Marie wanted to let them know, without actually voicing the words, that Tony too would do his best. But God forbid if things do not go well, it would not be Tony's fault if Frank did not come out of that prison alive. *And what if Tony doesn't make it?*

"Hi. It's me, Tony," he spoke softly into the phone. "How are you?"

A long pause as Tony's eyes rested on Marie's. A great sadness filled them.

"I'm at my parents' house and I'm getting ready to head out. But I wanted to call and let you know that everything at this point seems to be okay." Tony rubbed at the knot of tension throbbing at the base of his neck. "Frank's holding his own from what I could tell." He sat down on the arm of the living room sofa. "Yes. I saw him through the scope of a .270 rifle and I've been watching him and the yard through a pair of binoculars. It's only a matter of time before the whole thing will be over with," he attempted to reassure his sister-in-law, while filled with much self-doubt about when it would indeed be over. "Try not to worry too much." Tony glanced over at his mother who was trying to dab dry the moistness under her bloodshot eyes. "I will. Yeah, thanks." Tony stood up and placed the phone back in its cradle as his mother rushed across the room and into his arms. Once again, she began to sob uncontrollably.

Gently, Tony tried to pull himself free. He could not hang around their house any longer. It was all too emotionally difficult for him and he had no idea what the next day's task would be. And he *had* to be ready for whatever it was that lie ahead. He could not afford to be so emotionally drained. Tony wished he could offer comfort to his mother, but he couldn't. He just needed to leave the house. "I got to get some sleep for tomorrow, Ma," he said in an extremely soft tone so as not to further upset Mrs. Strollo.

Tony's father walked up beside his wife and slipped his arm around her shoulders. Marie detected the uncertainty in Tony's eyes. She knew in his heart he wanted to promise his parents that Frank was fine and he'd be bringing him home safe and sound very soon. But those words could not be spoken for no one knew how it was all going to turn out. And Tony never made empty promises. Marie walked over to where Tony and his parents were standing and gently tried to remove her mother-in-law's arms from Tony.

"Come on, Ma. Please do not make it any more difficult for Tony than it already is," Marie spoke in a gentle, yet firm voice.

Tony tried to inch away and after much encouragement and some persuasion from Tony's father, Mrs. Strollo reluctantly released her hold on her son, still visibly upset and sobbing.

Tony and his father exchanged knowing glances as they shook hands, then embraced briefly. Tony and his Dad always could communicate without so much as saying a single word. And his father always showed him strong, but silent support for whatever Tony chose to do. Mr. Strollo clapped his son firmly on the back then slipped his arm back around his wife. "They trained him well. Anthony has had excellent training from both the Army and the State Police." He gave his wife a hug. "He'll do a good job."

Mr. Strollo looked at his son a long moment before speaking. "Take care, Anthony," he said, his voice breaking with emotion.

Knowing he was at his own emotional breaking point, Tony clasped Marie's hand in his and nodded his farewell to his parents. Before leaving their house, he said, "Don't worry, Ma. I'll bring Frank home. I'll get him out of there." *One way or another, Frank will be coming home*, Tony promised himself. *And God willing, he'll be coming home alive.*

They could hear Mrs. Strollo's crying as they quickly walked down the driveway toward the car. "Bring your brother home, Anthony!" she called out in between sobs. "Bring him home! Bring your brother home!"

Once they reached the car, Tony paused a moment to suck in a deep, long breath of fresh air blowing it out hard several seconds later. He gave Marie's hand a tight squeeze before heading over to open her car door. They could still hear his mother's cries, "Bring your brother home, Anthony!"

Tony stole one last glance at his parents' house. He saw them standing outside the front door; his mother sobbing and continuously calling out to him. Tony slid into the front seat and started the car. As he pulled away, he and Marie could hear his mother's distant cries, "Bring your brother home, Anthony!"

Those words would be imprinted in his memory forever.

On the ride back to Batavia, Tony gazed straight ahead at the oncoming lights of the traffic. Marie sensed his thoughts were miles away. She released a pent-up sigh of her own as a shudder ripped through her body.

Tony glanced over at her. "Are you all right?"

Marie rested her head back against the seat. "I don't know, Tony," she groaned. "That was some scene. How are *you*?"

Tony turned his attention back to the road ahead. "I'm fine...considering. Ma's pretty upset. I wish I could've said or done more...."

"Tony, she'll be all right. You can't worry about anything or anyone else right now. This is tough all around, but it's worse for you, and Frank. Your Dad will help console your mother. Right now you need to concentrate on you and what's happening over at Attica."

"Mmmm," replied Tony as he drove toward the hotel.

Marie turned her head and studied her husband's face as the passing lights reflected off his features. Even in the dark, she could see the tension tightening his every muscle. She was concerned that Tony's parents might not be aware of the potential danger to Tony. Even though it was Frank who was in the obvious danger, Marie knew there could well be impending hazards for Tony as well. Would his parents be able to handle the possibility of losing Tony should he not be able to return? Or God forbid, if they both died? Marie knew they really hadn't thought about that scenario. They honestly believed Tony was not in harm's way and would be returning Frank to them. But Marie knew too well the dangers police officers often faced. The possibility of death went with the job. She should know. Her father had been a cop for 25 years. The fear was just there all the time. It never went away.

Back at the Holiday Inn's parking lot, Tony turned off the engine as he turned to face his wife. He smiled at her momentarily before gazing past her at the bright lights shining from the hotel. She could read his thoughts, they were miles away...at Attica... with Frank.

"Perhaps we'll be called out in the middle of the night...?" There was almost a hopeful tone to his voice. Hopeful and eager to resolve the horrible situation that had befallen the usually quiet little village of Attica, New York. A small town where neighbors were friends, and your friends were your neighbors.

Marie slid across the seat and wrapped her arms around her husband, desperately fighting the urge to never let him go. She was struggling to be a good cop's wife. She had to hold it together for Tony, the boys, and herself. It was important to Marie to be supportive of Tony. He had so many people depending on him that she wanted him to be able to depend on her, should he need to. "Try to get some sleep, Tony," she said bravely. "I think you're going to need it."

Tony turned to face Marie. He saw the worry and fear masked behind her false bravado, and he loved her for it. *And for much, much more.* He leaned over and gently kissed her before getting out of the car. He slammed the door shut as Marie slid behind the steering wheel. She lowered the window and smiled up at Tony as she turned the key in the ignition. Somewhere in the distance a truck's airhorn sounded, echoing in the night. Tony slapped the car's roof twice and grinned at Marie before she slowly drove out of the parking lot. He shoved his hands deep into his trouser pockets and stood in the lot watching the two rear lights of the car drive away until they were just tiny red specs in the blackness of the night.

A group of people emerged laughing from the hotel's entrance.

Alone, Tony allowed his shoulders to droop as he turned and walked solemnly back toward the brightly lit Holiday Inn. *What will tomorrow bring?* he wearily pondered. He did not know. No one knew. All Tony was certain of at that very moment as he shuffled his way through the main lobby, oblivious to all the people, was that he was extremely exhausted and desperately desired a nice, soft bed. Tony boarded the empty elevator and punched the floor button as he rested his body back against the coolness of the walls. The rocking and swaying motion of the elevator lulled Tony into a false sense of slumber. As the doors pulled open and Tony was greeted by a rush of air, he forced his eyes open and exited into the long hall where he proceeded to his room. At the door, he was greeted by his roommate. All Tony could manage was a weak smile as he dropped down onto the welcoming mattress.

As the softness enveloped his body, Tony's eyes refused to close. His mind was still replaying and racing through the events of the past two days. He was afraid he could not turn it off, even to sleep. And what if he did fall asleep? Would he oversleep?

Visions of his grieving parents and the sound of fear in his sister-in-law's voice over the phone haunted his last waking moments of the day.

Oh, God help me! his mind screamed.

Finally, it was the end of one very long day...the second one.

Saturday, September 11, 1971. A whole afternoon and part of an evening would pass before...the inmates' original demands were fashioned into proposals the state was willing to accept.

Major concessions were made, but sometimes they were heavily qualified.

Unknown to the observers, while these negotiations were taking place, those around the Commissioner favoring armed intervention were unexpectedly presented with new information they could use to bolster their argument. It came late that afternoon from an inmate who used a steel pipe to fight his way through surprised rebel security guards into A-block, which was held by the State Police. Correction guards fired tear gas into the passageway behind him to cover his flight.

After that, officials would sometimes indicate... that they had independent sources of information about inmates sharpening poles into spears and digging trenches.

As the hours wore on inconclusively, rumors of atrocities by the rebels gained wide currency among guards, troopers and even high officials. The most lurid of these...that a hostage had been emasculated— was heard and believed as early as Saturday.

A surgeon who had been making daily visits to D-Yard, heard...a report that inmates had forced two hostages into a bathroom, thrown wood in after them and set it on fire.

That same evening the doctor had himself been menaced and briefly detained by an inmate leader. He also described what he interpreted as a pattern of "psychological deterioration" of the prisoner population.

Two inmates suffered fits that evening, two more collapsed from nervous pressure and another went rigid in what appeared to be a catatonic state.

A one-armed (inmate) attempted suicide with a knife and had to be restrained by the leader. ...Other inmates were placed in a makeshift mental ward set up by the (inmate) leadership in its tent city, where some were injected with sedatives taken from the prison hospital.

To the Correction Officials, D-Yard seemed to be veering toward bedlam.

October 4, 1971   *The New York Times*
New York   "The Attica Revolt: Hour-By-Hour"
                         Joseph Lelyveld, Francis X. Clines,
                         Michael T. Kaufman and
                         James M. Markham

CHAPTER 5

Day Three: The Wait
Saturday, September 11, 1971

* * *

Tony and his detail began the third day much the same as the previous one. At his post on the second floor of A-Block, Tony sipped a cup of coffee while watching D-Yard through the barred windows. He saw that Albany headquarters had sent down photographers to shoot pictures for the State Police. Tony laughed as he watched them photograph *everything*.

He was greeted by another trooper who was rolling up the sleeves to his uniform shirt. "I didn't even unpack from State Fair duty in Syracuse," he informed Tony as he shook his head. "And here I am. There's quite a few of us who just got back from ten-day duty there."

Tony knew that wouldn't do a hell of a lot for morale, especially when they all would be under tight scrutiny from the higher-ups.

Another trooper joined them, adjusting his riot helmet. "I just heard that one of the hostages got dragged through the yard and because he wasn't moving fast enough, the inmate brutally beat the shit out of him until blood came pouring out of the guy's ears and nose."

They stood in silence a moment; stunned, angered, and out of respect for the hostage.

NYS Troopers checking Cell Block Area

*Photograph courtesy of
Anthony R. Strollo*

"We're into the third day here," another trooper announced as he joined them. "I just don't understand why we're wasting so much time waiting around."

They all looked out the window to the chaotic yard below.

"Shit," one swore as he took in the sight of scattered make-shift tents from sheets, blankets, whatever the inmates could get their hands on. There were piles of litter and garbage tossed among dirty mattresses in between several small campfires. Throughout the yard the inmates; some dressed in the hostages' confiscated uniforms, some in stolen religious garb, while others donned helmets and wrapped material around their heads and faces. In the hostage circle sat the men. Some men were blindfolded with their hands and feet bound with strips of cloth. They sat on the damp dirt, their bodies slumped over in defeat. Tony heard one trooper next to him suck in a sharp breath. He did not need to raise his binoculars to know what the man saw. The scene had been branded into his memory.

"My God," the trooper said in a mere whisper-like voice.

And through it all, the photographers shot photos.

Tony turned to watch another trooper roll his sleeves. Many of the men followed suit after playing the waiting game for so many days. Usually their dress code was extremely strict, but no one was going to give the troopers a hard time about appearances. Not after three days of waiting around.

The inmates' demands and negotiations were being dealt with by the committees and representatives from both sides, making Tony wonder just how long it could all go on. Everyone wanted to know why they were into the third day of a riot situation with one guard already dead and others being held hostage and facing the grim possibility of death. And the administration was allowing it to go on. Why? Why didn't they send in the troops? To Tony and the others, it seemed to be a major waste of time just to be waiting...and waiting...and waiting...and waiting. What were they waiting for? Another guard or hostage to be killed? Or what? Why? Everybody Tony worked with was anxious to resolve the situation. But what was the hold-up? That was the twenty-million dollar question.

As Tony waited he thought about how one never knew what the job would bring from one day to the next. Tony believed he had to just take it all one day at a time to survive. He couldn't be bothered wasting precious time worrying about what might happen to him on the job. He just did his work to the best of his ability, and he enjoyed doing so.

But sometimes fate can sneak up on one. Death was once again, literally, at his doorstep. Only this time it would be death from a riot situation and not as he had come to know it from his first fatal car accident investigation when he had been a newly assigned trooper to the Geneseo station two years earlier.

Tony had been one of the first troopers on the scene of a two-car accident that early morning on Route 15 in Livingston

County. As he approached the scene, he could see debris scattered all over the center of the highway. A tractor-trailer driver had pulled his rig off the road and was directing traffic around the two vehicles that had collided in the center of the road. It appeared to Tony that the one car with out-of-state plates had crossed over the solid, double-yellow no passing zone lines and hit the other vehicle head on. Tony immediately radioed for assistance and called for the Bureau of Criminal Investigation (BCI) to respond to the scene with a camera. Within minutes, the Station Commander Sergeant Henry Smith* was on the scene. BCI Investigator Joe Andolina* was also on the scene taking photos and acquiring identification from all those involved. Andolina was a quiet type of guy, short and stocky with a full head of black hair. Tony mused how much he reminded him of the actor who played *Cannon* in the old television series.

Tony approached the vehicles and peered in. It wasn't a pretty scene. The car with the local plate had one deceased male lying over the front seat of the automobile. The deceased looked to be about in his early forties and was covered in blood. Andolina leaned in through the driver's side window and carefully retrieved the man's wallet, obtaining his identification from the driver's license. The address of the deceased was just a couple of miles away from the accident scene.

Investigator Andolina handed the license to Tony. "Here, kid." Tony took the license. "Go make the next of kin notification. It's part of the job. You might as well get to learn it now as you start your State Police career," Andolina advised Tony in a direct order tone.

Tony stared down at the license a moment before seeking out the sergeant to inform him of where he was to go. Tony then spotted the local town judge observing the accident investigation from the sidelines. Tony knew the judge was familiar with the area, so he approached the man whom he had met only a few months before. "Judge Bolten*," he called out.

Judge Bolten was a tough judge who kept everyone in their proper place and he let the public know he was the boss in his court. For a man about sixty, Tony thought he looked much younger.

The judge met him halfway. "What's up, Tony?" inquired Judge Bolten.

"I have an assignment to make a next of kin notification for this guy," Tony stated, motioning toward the wrecked car with the New York plates. "He has a Jones Road address." Tony handed the deceased's license to the judge.

Glancing over the license, Judge Bolten nodded his head before handing it back to Tony. "Jones Road is just a couple of miles south of here. The guy was probably on his way to work. I could take a ride with you to show you where the place is. It shouldn't take long."

"Let me advise Sergeant Smith," Tony said as he turned and walked over to the sergeant.

"Sergeant Smith," called Tony. "I'm going to make next of kin notification. Judge Bolten said he would ride along to show me where the residence is."

"Okay," responded Sergeant Smith. "Don't take all day. Get to the point." The Sergeant hesitated a brief moment. "There is never an easy way to break the news," he advised Tony.

Tony and Judge Bolten slid into the troop car and headed south.

"Just down the road here we will make a left turn," the judge informed Tony as he pointed in the direction.

Approaching Jones Road, Tony clicked on his left turn signal, then reached for the police radio. Speaking into the microphone, Tony announced, "5-0-2-0 to Geneseo." 5020 was the number of Tony's troop car.

"Geneseo on," a male dispatcher's voice answered.

"5-0-2-0 Geneseo, I'll be out of the car on Jones Road to make a notification," Tony informed the dispatcher.

"Acknowledged 5-0-2-0."

Tony turned to the judge. "Judge, I never did this before." He hesitated a brief moment before continuing. "I know they are going to take it hard...and I can't stay here all day with them." Tony looked to the judge for some support. This was one matter Tony was not all that anxious to attend to.

Judge Bolten nodded his head in agreement then glanced out the window at the row of houses. "Let's try the house next door to the Reynolds'*. Maybe they know them and could accompany us to assist the family."

"Good idea," Tony agreed. "It's only 7:50 a.m. I hope they're up."

As Tony exited the car, he positioned his Stetson on his head as he and the judge approached the neighbor's house. Tony sucked in a deep breath before knocking on the front door. He was relieved when a woman in her mid-fifties answered.

"Could I help you, Officer?" she asked, a nervous edge to her voice.

"I hope so, Ma'am. I have some bad news to give the family next door and I was wondering if you know them and would be willing to accompany us when we break it to them?" Tony paused for a brief moment. "I am sure they will need some help."

Tony knew he saw the briefest expression of relief cross the woman's face when she heard the news was not for her family. But just as quickly, she was overcome with concern and worry for her neighbors.

"I'll be more than happy to help. The Reynolds have three daughters and are wonderful neighbors." The woman spoke as if she were in a trance. Tony knew that the mere sight of an unsolicited Trooper on one's doorstep was enough to alarm a person, let alone hear one state that he was the bearer of bad news, especially at such an early hour.

The neighbor continued as her eyes nervously darted from Tony to the judge then back to Tony. "Mr. Reynolds has probably already left for work," she said glancing down at her watch. "And their three daughters should be leaving for school soon." The woman's voice hung in the air, asking the unspoken.

Tony cleared his throat before answering her in a quiet voice. "The news I must tell them is that Mr. Reynolds was just killed in an automobile accident."

The woman's hand flew to her mouth as her eyes widened in horror. "Oh my God!" she cried. She was visibly shaken from the news. "It will certainly be difficult for them...," she said in a mere whisper while shaking her head in denial. She glanced next door at the Reynolds' house, tears slipping down her cheeks. "...such a wonderful family...and how those girls just loved their father...." The woman's voice cracked. "This is not good," she said looking back at Tony. "I'll do what I can."

Slowly, the trio made their way to the Reynolds' front door. Tony heard the commotion of the girls getting ready inside for school as he reached out to ring the door bell. He wished he could have been bringing this family good news instead of the worst possible kind every family dreaded receiving.

The judge and the neighbor stood on the steps behind Tony, waiting for him to break the news.

A lady answered the door with a puzzled look on her face, similar to her neighbor's reaction upon seeing Tony in uniform accompanied by the judge.

"Mrs. Reynolds?" Tony asked, standing in the doorway. He always knew what reaction to expect from people. A Trooper was indeed a formidable presence. Especially at 8:00 in the morning.

"Yes, I'm Mrs. Reynolds," the lady responded looking at all three of them with great concern. "What's wrong?"

Tony swallowed hard. "I'm afraid I have some bad news for you, Mrs. Reynolds."

The woman stared directly at Tony. "W-what is it?"

Tony could tell she was fast becoming frantic. And rightfully so.

"May I come in, please?" Tony asked softly as he stepped inside the door, removing his hat.

"Yes," Mrs. Reynolds replied numbly as she backed up to allow Tony, the judge and her neighbor in. Mrs. Reynolds studied her friend's face a moment.

Tony could see that Mrs. Reynolds knew this was a serious matter. He did not want to prolong her agony. "Please, sit down," Tony quietly instructed her. After she sat down on the edge of the sofa, Tony broke the news to her. "Mrs. Reynolds," he began softly. "Your husband was just killed in an automobile accident on the way to work this morning." *There*, thought Tony somberly. *I did it. The truth is out.* Tony could not have been prepared for just how shitty he truly felt at that very moment.

"Oh, no!" she shouted, tears filling her eyes. "It can't be true," she sobbed as her daughters came rushing into the room. The girls, aged twelve to seventeen, all stared at Tony in shock and disbelief. "Please," Mrs. Reynold's cried. "Tell me it's not true."

The oldest daughter was in a state of panic as she glared at Tony while hugging her sobbing mother. "Are you sure it was my father?" She studied Tony's serious face as he nodded. Then her eyes darted to the judge and then to her neighbor, who was also crying by this time. The girl's eyes filled with tears turned to her mother and hysterical sisters. "It couldn't have been...." She looked back to Tony. "Please," she cried. "Tell me it's not true!"

Tony knew conducting a next of kin notification was going to be a difficult task. He just didn't know *how* difficult and heartwrenching until that very moment. "I'm afraid it is true, Miss," he stated as he held his hat in front of him, maintaining a tighter than usual grip on it. "There has been positive identification...I don't know of any easier way of telling you." Tony motioned to the lady from next door. "Your neighbor is here to help and do what she can for you. I must leave to continue my investigation." Tony turned to leave, placing his Stetson back on his head. He paused to glance back at the grieving family. "I am sorry," he solemnly stated before leaving the residence with the judge.

Pinching his eyes shut for a moment, Tony prayed he would not have to make any next of kin notifications as a result of the riot situation here at Attica. *Especially to my own family and friends.*

Tony saw many different politicians and group leaders coming into the prison. Everyone thought they had *the* answer, but apparently nobody did because the troopers were still at their posts...waiting.

At one point while waiting up on the second floor at his post on A-Block, one senior trooper Tony knew had about ten years on the job and was a true straight-laced, by-the-book type of trooper who believed in the idea that what was right was right; had finally become totally disgusted at the idea of the inmates having control over the institution. From where he was standing, he spun around and with a mighty force kicked out at a small metal table, sending it clanging loudly against the wall. "Let's get this damned thing over with," he swore fiercely.

One of the sergeants stepped over to him and placed a hand on the trooper's shoulder in a firm manner. "Relax," he spoke in a calm voice. "We're all up tight." The sergeant motioned to Tony with a quick nod of his head. "Look at Tony. His brother is out there. We're all hanging around, waiting to get this thing over with. Who would want to get it over with more than us...?" The sergeant glanced over his shoulder and met Tony's stare. "...more than Tony?" The sergeant patted him on the back. "Just stay calm. We're going to get this over with." After the sergeant walked away, the trooper lifted his head to look at Tony. Without saying a word, he sighed and nodded to Tony that he had things under control.

Tony acknowledged his understanding with a nod of his head before turning his attention back out to the yard. He raised the binoculars up to his eyes to conduct his visual scan. Tony did not blame the other trooper for losing his cool. Things were beginning to drag on way too long, and Tony knew he wasn't the only trooper concerned for the well-being of the hostages. Would they be kept alive? And if so, for how long? The only reason the hostages were alive was because the rebels were using them as a bargaining chip. What if the negotiations failed? Would they then kill each and every hostage? They already killed Timmy. If all communications broke down, what would stop them from killing again? And what about the physical condition of the hostages? From what Tony could see, some of them looked like they could use medical attention. But how seriously were they injured? Tony could not understand why the inmates didn't just turn themselves in. They had to know by that point that there were over 500 troopers positioned around the prison just waiting for the order to be given to go in and meet force with force.

Letting the binoculars fall down to his chest, Tony leaned against the wall while recalling the words of Marie's father, who was a member of the Buffalo P.D.: "In a tough situation expect the worst," he had advised Tony. "But hope for the best."

Good words of wisdom, thought Tony. In this situation, the worst would be going in and finding Frank and the others dead, and getting killed in the process.

Tony pushed himself off the wall and gazed back out through the bars. He was aware that his detail would be standing up against approximately 1,300 inmates during the initial retaking. *Some odds*, he thought grimly. Still, Tony believed if he had to die, then at least it would be for a good cause. It would be while attempting to free the hostages. It was his job and no matter what he was to be faced with, Tony would do it in support of the criminal justice system he believed in. He knew he had to go in and do the best damned job he could, and be at peace with himself about it.

What will be, will be.

Still, Tony silently prayed that they could move in and get the whole stinking mess over with and have everyone come out of it okay.

* * *

Marie nervously paced the kitchen floor as she sipped at about her hundreth cup of coffee since the insurrection began. The radio, as usual, was playing in the background. She paused to listen as the announcer proceeded to give out detailed information regarding the position of the troopers outside the prison, what weapons they had, their intent on using tear gas dropped from helicopters, etcetera. She turned to stare incredulously at the radio as the man's voice crackled over the airwaves. She slammed her cup down on the counter causing the creamy liquid to splash out over the Formica top. She could feel the anger well up inside her as she clenched her teeth while running a hand through her hair. *How could they be so thoughtless?* her mind screamed. *That should be confidential information!*

Joseph entered the kitchen whistling a perky tune while carrying a laughing Michael in his arms. A.J. dashed in ahead of him. Joseph saw the distressed look on his sister's face and immediately stopped whistling. "What's up, Marie?" he asked, his voice full of concern.

Marie stared at him for a long moment, her eyes dark with anger as she marched past him to the wall phone. She grabbed the phone book off the counter and began page flipping in an erratic manner. "I can't believe they're giving out such detailed information," she proclaimed disgustedly.

Joseph slid Michael down into his high chair and opened a

cabinet door to remove some cereal bowls. A.J. grabbed a box of his favorite cereal and started hopping up and down next to his uncle, waiting impatiently for a bowl. Joseph paused to watch his sister throw the phone book back down on the counter and reach for the phone.

"Maybe you shouldn't be listening to the radio all of the time, Marie."

Marie dialed the number, glancing over her shoulder at her brother. "I just want to hear what they say. It's the only way I feel connected to Tony."

Joseph shook his head as he poured out the boys' cereal. Michael reached across the top of his high chair and grabbed a handful of dry cereal, stuffing some into his little mouth as half of it clattered to the floor. "Do you want something to eat, Sis?" asked Joseph as he splashed some milk into the bowls and handed each child a spoon.

"I can't eat, Joseph. My stomach is all tied up in knots over this situation at Attica." She offered him a brief smile. "Thanks, anyway." The radio once again caught her attention and her smile faded fast as she heard them continue to give out detailed information on the State Police strategy. Marie's foot began to tap impatiently as she waited for the radio station to pick up their phone. "Come on, come on. Someone pick up!" Marie sighed deeply, then stood at abrupt attention. "Hello?" she spoke into the phone, continuing on without stopping. "I'm calling to complain about your broadcasting—"

"Marie?" the female voice on the other end replied. "Marie, is that *you*?"

Marie's mouth fell open in a confused state of shock. "W-what?"

"Marie, this is Nancy*."

"Nancy? How did I get you? I was calling the radio station...?" Marie had dialed her good friend instead of the station.

"You dialed the wrong number! The radio station's number

is only one digit different from mine, so hang up and try again," said Nancy.

"I'm sorry, Nancy." Marie rubbed a finger at her throbbing temple. She dropped her arm down to her side, slapping her leg. "I can't believe I dialed you by mistake. I'm just so darn angry that they're broadcasting such news. They shouldn't be giving out every move the State Police have planned like that."

"Well, you go tell them what you think, Marie!" her friend added enthusiatically.

Joseph glanced up as Marie hung up the phone and rested her head against the wall for a long moment before picking the receiver back up to dial the correct number. "I can't believe all this!" she said to her brother in sheer frustration. Once again Marie tapped her foot as she waited for someone at the radio station to answer the phone. "Yes," she stated into the receiver after hearing the party announce that it was indeed the station this time. "I'd like to make a suggestion for the station to stop broadcasting every move of the State Police outside of the prison."

Joseph grinned and gave Marie the thumb's up sign.

"Well," she continued on in a very stern voice. "The inmates can't see way down the road. They don't know what weapons the State Police have or that they are planning to use tear gas...." Marie grew angrier as she clenched her fist. "Well, *I'm* sorry, but did you ever hear of using the element of surprise? The inmates *do* have radios, you know." A long pause. "Thank *you!*" Marie slammed the phone down as she turned to face her brother. Both of her sons had stopped eating and were staring at their Mommy.

Marie saw their worried little faces and forced a smile on her face. "It's okay, boys. Keep eating. Mommy's just a little mad at the radio people for talking too much." She motioned with a sweep of her hand. "Go on, eat your cereal." She looked over at

Joseph and frowned. The last thing she wanted to do was upset her boys.

The radio continued to broadcast news updates, but Marie did notice that they had become a bit more vague in detail since her phone call to the station.

For whatever reasons, according to one of the broadcasts, the retaking and rescue mission had been postponed.

Marie sighed deeply.

* * *

Over at Attica, rumors circulated throughout the day that the State Police would be going in at any moment. Tony knew his group would be the first to go in. Knowing that the time might be drawing near, Tony decided he did not want to go back to the hotel or to his residence that evening. So when his shift for the day was over, he located Lieutenant Arthur elsewhere in A-Block and the two stepped off to the side to speak privately.

"Sir," Tony began. "It's the end of my shift and I would like to request to stay here at the prison for the night after I'm relieved from duty. I can rejoin my detail in the morning," Tony stated.

"I'll give you permission to stay," responded the Lieutenant, but added in a stern, gruff voice, "but remember, you've *got* to be ready for duty tomorrow. You are not getting any special overtime for this," he advised. "And you're on your own while staying here."

"Yes, Sir. Thank you, Lieutenant." Tony realized Lieutenant Arthur knew him well enough to know that no matter what, Tony would indeed be ready for his tour. He only sounded tough to let Tony know he wasn't going to get any special treatment or be cut any slack. But in actuality, Tony mused, the Lieutenant really was giving him a break by letting him stay the night at the facility. Should all hell break loose during the night, Tony knew the Lieutenant understood that he needed to be there, *had* to be there...for his brother and for the other hostages he once worked with and cared about. Not to mention, Tony would be a great asset during the rescue mission as he knew the hostages from the inmates from his days as a C.O. It did not matter if the hostages wore inmate clothing, Tony would recognize them. They were his co-workers and neighbors. He would know them without a doubt.

Having received permission to remain at the prison for the night, Tony returned to his post at A-Block. At approximately 10:30 p.m., the Warden visited the cellblock with some officials. Tony escorted them through A-Block. They stopped and the Warden and the officials looked out the windows into the yard below.

The scene was ominous. As Tony raised his binoculars to his eyes, he saw the scattered campfires throughout the yard, their orange and yellow flames leaping upward, reaching for the black sky. The tower lights illuminated the yard in an almost eerie manner with the backdrop of tents and fires as almost 1,300 inmates occupied the yard.

Tony searched the darkened yard for the hostage circle. His sights set on it, he could not locate Frank. *Please God*, he silently prayed as a shiver shot down his spine. *Please let him still be alive.*

Tony escorted the Warden and his associates back out through A-Block, all the time wondering where in the hell his brother was. Where did they take him? Why wasn't he in the hostage circle with the others? Was he ill? Dead? Or just out of Tony's sight?

"Thank you, Tony," the Warden offered before leaving.

Tony leaned back against the wall and stared after the Warden and his entourage. It had been a very short visit. Tony did not know if that meant the troops would be going in soon, or not. And the Warden certainly did not offer any information to him . Tony crossed his arms in front of his chest. He was curious to know if they were planning on retaking the prison during the night. He knew there would be definite pros and cons regarding a night move. On the positive side, the inmates would definitely be taken by surprise, never expecting the police to storm the facility in the dark. While on the negative side, there was a greater risk of casualties because of limited vision in the darkness.

Tony sighed deeply as he adjusted his helmet. He stood straight and tried to roll the tension out from his shoulders. He then headed back to the second floor, passing another trooper who had been relieved from his shift for the night. In passing, they nodded to each other as the trooper passed his Ithaca Model 37 shotgun to Tony.

"Thanks," Tony replied as he held onto the gun and continued patrolling the second floor of the cellblock until he located a discarded mattress he could use to rest on for the night. The area had been trashed. It wasn't too difficult to find a mattress as several cells had been turned upside down and totally destroyed during the initial insurrection. Clad in his riot helmet, binoculars securely hanging around his neck, gas mask in one hand and the shotgun cradled in his arm, Tony stretched out across the stripped mattress ready to rest for the night.

He closed his eyes, but all he saw was the blindfolded face of his brother sitting in the hostage circle with his hands tied, just waiting...waiting to be rescued...or waiting to die. Or was he already dead? The fact that Tony had been unable to locate Frank the last time he scanned the yard, kept nagging at him. *Where in the hell are you, Frank?* Tony tried to block out the horrible scenarios that were being played out in his mind's eye.

A sudden tug on his shotgun sent Tony's pulse pounding through his body. Automatically, his hold on the weapon became death-like in nature as his body broke out in a cold sweat. Tony felt his heart lunge as though it would burst out of his chest. Keeping his grip on the shotgun, his body tensed like that of a wild animal about to pounce on its prey. Tony snapped open his eyes to see a dark figure looming above him.

It was a fellow trooper.

His senses clearing, Tony could only stare at the man.

The other trooper took a step back, surprised to see Tony awake. "I just wanted to use your shotgun since you were sleeping."

Tony relaxed his muscles as he drew in a deep breath, then blew it out hard as if to exorcise the demons running through his mind. "I am *not* sleeping," Tony stated firmly. "I am ready to go in at any time." Tony tightened his hold on the weapon. "So this is *my* shotgun. You'll have to find one someplace else."

After the other man left, Tony once again closed his weary eyes as his pulse finally returned to a normal pace. The hollow echo of voices vibrated through the halls. An occasional loud chant from out in the yard would boom up in volume and reach Tony's ears. In the distance, Tony could hear the grinding mechanics of a metal gate clanging everytime it open and closed.

Tony knew he would never be able to fall into a restful sleep even though his body and mind were completely exhausted. As he inhaled deeply, the strong stench of stale cigarettes mingled with the musty odor of the cell filled his nostrils as more distant voices haunted his slumber. Scenes from the yard...scenes of his brother and the other hostages flashed through his mind.

As the third long day drew to a close, Tony finally drifted off into an uneasy state of rest, his ears tuned for sound...any sound.

Sunday, September 12, 1971. ...to the state, word that the inmates had not accepted the package was a signal that the negotiating committee could virtually be counted out.

Earlier that afternoon, a guard watching D-Block, which was entirely in rebel hands, saw an inmate he recognized appear at a third-floor window...the guard heard the inmate shout: "They're cutting my throat!"

The inmate...a convicted robber and one of three men arrested by the rebel leadership on Friday. As the guard watched, so the account goes,.....(the inmate) then climbed down to the second story on bars that run vertically along the face of the building. There he was grabbed and pulled back into the cellblock.

His body would be discovered Monday morning.

October 4, 1971	*The New York Times*
New York	"The Attica Revolt: Hour-By-Hour"
	Joseph Lelyveld, Francis X. Clines,
	Michael T. Kaufman and
	James M. Markham

By now, all the law enforcement personnel knew that the brother of Trooper Anthony Strollo, Correction Officer Frank Strollo, was being held hostage. It was disheartening and frustrating to the waiting officers to accept the fact that he and other hostages would have to spend another night...(at the prison).

1987	*History of the New York State*
New York	*Police 1917 - 1987.*
	"Attica - 1971 - LeBastille
	Extraordinaire"
	Sgt. Pamela T. Shelton

CHAPTER 6

Day Four: Questions Without Answers
Sunday, September 12, 1971

* * *

Sunday morning arrived too soon as Tony once again scanned D-Yard through the binoculars from the barred window up on the second floor of A-Block. Things the previous night seemed ominous to Tony as sleep had eluded him most of the night. When he was able to doze off in between the loud clanging of gates, the distant voices bellowing from out in the yard and the hollow voices that echoed through the prison, it was a fitful sleep. There were moments when he questioned why he even tried, except he knew he had to in order to avoid physical and emotional exhaustion.

Lieutenant Arthur approached him. "How did your night go?" he asked as he handed Tony a cup of hot coffee.

Tony readily accepted the steaming brew. He could use a good shot of caffeine. The rest he did get was sufficient, and though he knew his appearance lacked the usual shine with being bleary-eyed and in need of a good shave, he was alert and ready-to-go just the same. Adrenaline had that affect on him. He could feel the energy pumping back through his body. "Just fine, Lieutenant," Tony responded before sipping the coffee.

"Thank you for letting me stay overnight."

The Lieutenant scrutinized Tony for a long moment. "Do you think you can make it through the day, Tony?"

Without hesitation, Tony replied, "Yes, Sir."

"If you're tired, we can relieve you from duty," offered the Lieutenant.

Tony shook his head as he raised up the styrofoam cup. "No, Sir. I'll be just fine," he replied before taking another swallow of the coffee. Tony watched the Lieutenant as he walked down the long, dismal hall of the cellblock. When he was out of sight, Tony turned back around to keep his now-standard vigil of D-Yard as he leaned his shotgun against his leg. He felt a bit calmer since first spotting his brother in the yard earlier that morning. *I'm here, Frank. I'm here.*

Another time during the day, the Chief Inspector for the State Police entered A-Block to visit with Tony. The time was definitely nearing for the order to be given for the troopers to move in. As Tony and the inspector viewed the situation down in the yard, they observed the inmates setting up reinforced barricades that were erected specifically so that the troopers would have a difficult time getting through. Glancing down the corridor toward the catwalk, they saw that steel tables had also been tipped over and covered in barbwire fencing.

The Chief Inspector spoke first. "How do you feel about going in?" he asked Tony, knowing the situation involving Tony's brother as one of the hostages.

Yeah, how do I feel about it? Tony ran through the questions in his own mind. *How do I feel about Frank sitting out there, an unarmed target? How do I feel about carrying out my own brother's dead body? How do I feel about going home to tell his wife and kids that he's dead? How do I feel about telling Ma that her first born would never be coming to visit her again? And how do I feel about returning home to face my own wife and kids having failed at the rescue attempt? Yes, Tony, how do you feel?* His mind searched for the answers as he stood quietly deep in thought, staring off at nothing in particular.

"You do realize the inmates are saying that with the first shot fired, all the hostages will die?" continued the Chief Inspector. "How do you feel about that, Tony?"

Tony studied the inspector as he spoke. He knew the man was genuinely interested in Tony's thoughts and point-of-view of the situation at hand.

"Tony? How do you feel about your brother being a hostage out there?"

Yes, Tony. How do you feel? he thought silently as he glanced back down at the yard.

The Chief Inspector continued his line of questioning. "Do you still want to go in?"

Tony felt his heart pound wildly in his chest. During all the time spent doing this detail, Tony kept himself from thinking about the very questions the Chief Inspector had now placed before him. Tony had to confront his deepest thoughts and fears. And he had to do so now before the inspector. Tony drew in a deep breath and straightened his stance as he looked directly at the Chief Inspector.

"Yes, Sir, I do still want to go in." Tony stole another glance at the yard. "We can not let the inmates continue this any longer. We are now into the fourth day."

The inspector stepped alongside Tony and followed his gaze to the chaotic yard below. He continued on, his voice low but stern. "You have military background. How do you propose we get through that barrier fast enough to save the hostages?" he asked with a quick jerk of his head toward the barricades the rebel inmates had constructed.

Tony crossed his arms in front of his chest. His voice was dead serious. "Sir," he began as he looked directly into the inspector's eyes. "You give me an M-79 grenade launcher and I'll show you just how fast we can get through that barrier. We'll wipe them out in a second." *Just blow the damn barrier to hell.*

The Chief Inspector turned to face Tony, arching a brow at him. "I guess you really *do* want to get this thing over with."

"Hell, these people are suffering. Their families are suffering," responded Tony as he looked down at the hostage circle. He shook his head in total disgust. "It's been four days...four *long* days." He looked back at the inspector. "It's beyond time for talk. Beyond time for any more negotiations. It is time to take back the prison and free those hostages."

"Okay," the inspector replied thoughtfully as he nodded at Tony. "I know your feelings. Even though there is a good chance your brother may be killed, you still want to go in there."

Tony scanned the yard, narrowing his eyes as he watched the inmates parade around in holy garments and officers' clothing. They desecrated everything that was sacred. They desecrated religion. They desecrated their home. They desecrated lives. They turned the prison yard into a horrible war zone. "Yes, Sir," Tony said in a far-away voice as he viewed the despoliation in the yard below. "Yes, Sir," he reaffirmed. "I still want to go in there." Tony raised the binoculars to his eyes. "We have to get this damned thing over with."

Tony spotted his brother, blindfolded like the others, sitting elbow-to-elbow with the other men in a circular formation. They all had their hands bound in front of them as their shoulders slumped in despair and dejection, stripped of their rights and dignity. Even the proudest of men would feel beaten being at the hands of rebel inmates after four long days.

Tony's jaw twitched, as he thought about how those men had families waiting for them. Praying for them. Praying and waiting for something...even a tiny tidbit of hope. How many of those men's wives would become widows? How many children will become fatherless? How many mothers and fathers will lose a son? How many tears of sadness will be shed? How much blood had to be spilled in order for the rebels to feel that their united voice had been heard? Was sacrificing a human life worth a gripe about showers? Did the desire for better conditions justify the taking of a life to prove a point?

Even though Tony knew the majority of the inmates were incarcerated for serious and vicious crimes such as murder, manslaughter, rape, robbery - nobody got sent to Attica for a mere error in judgement - he could not believe they would want to bring down such a reign of terror onto themselves, their families as well as the hostages and their families.

In drawing attention to their demands for change, the rebel inmates had started up a runaway train that only they had the power to stop by surrendering themselves. But Tony knew they would never surrender because he knew many of the inmates and their attitudes from when he worked at Attica, guarding some of those very same men. They would let that runaway train crash first before they would ever consider surrendering. Tony did not want to allow that train to gain any more steam.

"We have to get it over with," he repeated to the Chief Inspector. "It's what my brother would want." He lowered the binoculars and turned to face the inspector. "I worked with most of those guys when I was here. I know how they felt about their job and the potential risks. I also know they would not want to die at the hands of their captors. They would want us to come in and end it. I know if it was me down there, I'd rather take my chances with the troops storming in and attempting a rescue than sit and wait to be killed by one of those rebels."

Long after the inspector had left, Tony maintained his watch over D-Yard. Standing there, he believed that in some way, he was guarding over Frank until the order came to move in. *Just hang in there, Frank.* Tony stared down at where his brother was, hoping that via some sort of mental telepathy, Tony's thoughts would somehow penetrate his brother's subconscious and give him some strength and hope during the final hours of the insurrection. *Please God*, Tony prayed. *Just let me get him out of this alive. Let everyone come out alive.*

After much talking and negotiating, tensions mounted between the inmates and the administration. Tony felt that the order to move in would be coming at any moment, but by the end of his shift Tony knew they would one again postpone sending in the troops until morning.

When his night shift relief arrived, Tony headed back to the Holiday Inn with his detail. Pretty certain the move wouldn't occur until morning, Tony had decided against seeking permission to remain at the facility-for another sleepless night.

Upon arriving at his room, Tony dropped down exhaustedly onto the bed as his thoughts drifted in and out of the past years of his life. First thoughts of Marie and the kids entered his mind. He wanted to reach over for the phone and call her...but he was so tired. Yet he could not keep from visualizing his family... and his big brother. Big brother who had always throughout life tried to protect Tony. Closing his eyes, Tony could see Frank sliding his arm around Tony's shoulder at the bus stop back when they were boys and Tony had wanted to run away...Tony could almost feel the warmth of Frank's strong arm around him....Tony smiled as he fondly recalled having the upper hand with Frank when he tumbled his big brother to the floor at his parents' house when he had come home on leave from the Army... and Tony recalled the days when the Strollo brothers were fellow correctional officers right there at Attica... *Attica!* Tony's mind screamed as his weary body flinched at the vision of Frank clothed in inmate garb, bound and blindfolded sitting on the damp earth with fellow hostages, waiting...waiting for...Tony? Tony could not fight the overwhelming feeling that Frank was waiting for his little brother to come in and rescue him.

That vision of Frank would be one Tony would never be able to erase from his memory. Never.

As four long days of waiting drew to a close, Tony began to drift off into an uneasy sleep as his own words haunted his dreams...

"We have to get it over with."

Monday September 13, 1971. The inmate who was seen Sunday being pulled back into the (third floor) cellblock, (his body) was discovered with more than 30 stab wounds and his throat cut. Nearby were two other bodies, one a convicted murderer showing the same pattern of multiple wounds. It was an unusual pattern, according to...(the) assistant Medical Examiner in New York who inspected the bodies - a pattern that is generally associated with a certain kind of psychopathic rage.

As originally drawn up, the plan for Monday morning called for an assault with no further warning to the inmates. The hope was to exploit the element of surprise to minimize loss of life among the 38 hostages who the authorities were convinced had only the slimmest chance of survival in an assault

"There was absolutely no doubt in anyone's mind that if we went in there, the guards would be killed," declared (an Assemblyman).

What finally outweighed this grim assessment were the conviction among the authorities that they had exhausted all acceptable options, a fear that the Attica rebellion could become epidemic in prisons throughout the state and nation, and the insistence of the tormented guards and townspeople that the time had come to "get it over with."

The inmates thought they were safe as long as they had the correction officers.

Flourishing their trump card, inmates led eight hostages - now bound and blindfolded - to the catwalk atop Times Square. Rebel leaders...had put each hostage in the charge of individual inmates.

Removed from this scene, in the Superintendent's office several hundred yards away, (the) Commissioner asked for the last

time: "Do you see any way we can avoid doing this (retaking)?"
The Superintendent and several Republican legislators were in
the room.

  No one answered.

October 4, 1971	*The New York Times*
New York	"The Attica Revolt: Hour-By-Hour"
	Joseph Lelyveld, Francis X. Clines,
	Michael T. Kaufman and
	James M. Markham

  ...the 189-man assault against the 1,281 rebels would begin.
Disgusted though the State Police were by the executioners they
could see through their telescopic sights, they were too well trained
to open fire prematurely and throw off the whole battle plan.

1972	Russell G. Oswald,
New York	Commissioner of Corrections of
	New York State during the
	Attica Riot. *Attica-My Story*

CHAPTER 7

Day Five: The Retaking of Attica
Monday, September 13, 1971

* * *

Day five began as a dismal and rainy morning as Tony and his detail once again began their shift at 6:00 a.m. They were briefed at approximately 8:00 a.m., then began making serious preparations for the pending retaking and rescue mission. It had now become an extremely critical time as all negotiations had failed and the rebel inmates demanded amnesty, and that was not going to be granted. Never.

Tony and his fellow members of the State Police began taping around the wrist area of their uniform sleeves as well as around the ankles of their trousers. This procedure would stop irritation of the skin from the tear gas that would be used. As Tony craned his neck to button the top of his shirt, word was given that a helicopter would drop the tear gas and the detail would then proceed out onto the A-Catwalk when the direct order was given.

Tony and his detail were positioned in A-Block. Shortly after 9:00 a.m., Tony received word that the final efforts in negotiations had failed. He pinched his eyes shut a moment as a chill shot through his body. *Okay, God,* he prayed. *This is it.* Tony envisioned his brother being killed at the hands of one of the executioners. Thoughts came firing through his brain. Thoughts of Frank's children. They were so young. How could he tell them that their Daddy would never be coming home again? That he would never be able to play with them or give them piggy-back rides anymore? How could he look into those innocent little faces and attempt to explain that their Uncle Anthony could not do anything to save their father?

Come on, Frank, just hold on. Tony glanced around at the rest of his detail, all poised and ready to move on a second's notice. *I'll be coming for you, Big Brother. I'll be coming in very soon now.*

Tony heard the Commissioner speaking with the inmates through the bars in a last-ditch effort before sending the troops in. Tony's heart pounded fiercely in his chest that he thought at any moment it would burst right out of his body. He could feel his adrenaline coursing through his body as every nerve ending throbbed throughout him in anxious anticipation. Tony sucked in a deep breath as he wiped a sweaty palm across the leg of his trousers. He overheard the Commissioner's final attempt at negotiating with the rebel inmates.

"Release the hostages now and we will continue negotiations in the mess hall," promised the Commissioner.

Tony gripped his gas mask in preparation as he glanced out through the barred windows to the yard below. Through the gray drizzle, a sense of genuine fear shot through him as he saw some of the hostages being taken up on the catwalks by their inmate executioners. The hostages were tied and had knives held to their throats. In the rain-soaked yard, inmates gathered about the wet makeshift shelters and washed-out campfires. They kept glancing up to where they knew certain troopers were posted as though they, too, sensed the end of the insurrection was drawing near.

He quickly conducted a scan of the hostage circle in search of his brother, his heart thudding against his chest. *Please, God.*

Don't let him be dead. There were, from Tony's quick calculations, at least 1200 inmates out in that yard against the 25 assaulting troopers for the initial retaking. Tony could not squelch the thought of the inmates taking them out and gaining possession of their weapons. It would not be impossible since the assaulting troopers were most definitely outnumbered by the rebelling inmates. Still, Tony felt that he was more than ready to go in. Now that the time had finally arrived, he felt better prepared to move in than he had even anticipated. After all the waiting and negotiating and waiting and negotiating, the time to go in with his fellow troopers and do what they were trained to do, had arrived. And hopefully, they would be able to save the lives of the hostages while doing so.

It was Tony's deepest belief that if he had only five minutes of life left in him upon entering the yard, then by God, he would do his very best for those five minutes. Tony, as well as his fellow troopers, knew full well the risk they were taking - they knew their detail chanced being overwhelmed by the large number of rioting inmates. But Tony also knew it would only be a matter of time before the back-up troopers would regain control of the prison.

Tony's detail would be the first to go in and make initial contact. It was his every intention to get through that yard to his brother, no matter where Frank was being held. At that very moment, Tony had absolutely no idea where his brother was. He did not know if the inmates had moved him up onto the catwalk, or if Frank was still back in D-Yard being held somewhere with the remainder of the hostages. The one other possibility Tony did not want to belabor was that Frank could already be dead.

Things in the yard were becoming very chaotic and confusing. Fear was in the air.

Tony felt afraid as well. Afraid for his brother. Afraid for the other hostages. Afraid for himself and his detail. And afraid for all their families. Tony took one more look through the binoculars and offered a silent prayer of protection for those men and for his detail. It was now only a matter of time before all of their lives would be changed forever, no matter what the outcome.

I do not want to be the bearer of bad news. Especially to my own family and friends.

Once again Tony heard the Commissioner address the rebel inmates. "Release the hostages or the State Police are coming in."

An inmate spokesman responded loudly to the commissioner. "Negative!" he shouted in a clear voice. "The hostages will die if the State Police come in," he threatened.

Upon hearing that, Tony believed Frank and the others did not have a chance to make it out alive.

Tony mentally prepared himself to break the news to his parents, to Frank's wife and kids. *If I make it out alive.*

The time had arrived. Tony prayed that Father Browning was around. He was going to be needed.

The four long days of waiting had come to a close. Tony pinched his eyes shut briefly as he offered one last silent prayer for his brother, the hostages, his family, his fellow troopers...and for himself.

Tony peered through the window. It was still raining. He then double-checked the taping on his uniform as he adjusted the top button once again on his shirt just to be certain that he was set.

The steady whir of helicopter blades sounded prominently as one flew low over the yard.

"We won!" Tony heard one inmate exclaim. "We called their bluff and won!"

"I don't want to die!" screamed a hostage as he was led up on the catwalk blindfolded, with a knife held to his throat by

Five hostages being held with knives at their throats by rioting inmates minutes before the State Police regained control of Attica Prison on September 13, 1971.

Photograph courtesy of Anthony R. Strollo

his inmate executioner.

Tony and his detail cleared their gas masks then donned them. Within seconds, at approximately 9:30 a.m., the gas was dropped from the helicopters and the order was given to move out.

The time has come, was Tony's last thought before they burst through to the outside.

* * *

Back home, Marie nervously paced the kitchen floor listening to the radio she had established a true love/hate relationship with. Just then, the radio announcer broadcasted that the helicopters had dropped tear gas and the State Police were moving in. A chill spread through her body. Marie froze as she heard the gunfire erupt right over the radio station! For the ensuing minutes, her entire world clung to the announcer's every word. As he spoke, Marie's mind literally tuned out the man's voice as her past dream came back to haunt her:

THE STEADY WHIR OF HELICOPTER BLADES CUT-TING THE AIR SOUNDED PROMINENTLY ABOVE SHOUTS AND GUNFIRE FROM BELOW IN WHAT APPEARED TO BE A YARD...A PRISON YARD.

"Oh no," she cried as she limply dropped down into a chair.

Joseph rushed to her side. "What is it, Marie?"

Marie could only stare blankly ahead. It was happening again. Another dream was coming true. Only this was a nightmare. Marie felt it all happening around her as she listened to the radio. She knew exactly what was going on over at Attica without actually being there.

She was living her nightmare.

INMATES WERE RUNNING RAMPANT RAISING HANDMADE WEAPONS OF GLASS AND STEEL, STRIKING OTHER INMATES AND UNIFORMED CORRECTIONAL OFFICERS

IT WAS A HORRIFIC SCENE....

Marie's nightmarish dream was coming true, and there wasn't a damned thing she could do to stop it.

Feeling sick, Marie doubled over in the chair. She threw her hands up to cover her ears. She did not want to hear any more. She just wanted it to stop. To go away.

Seeing how visibly shaken his sister had become, Joseph sprang up to turn off the radio. "I don't think it's such a good idea to—"

"No!" screamed Marie, her eyes wide as she leaped up from the chair. "I want to hear every word." She added in a quieter tone, "I mean, I don't *want* to, Joseph." Her eyes pleading with him. "I *need* to."

Joseph frowned as he left the radio on and went to his sister's side. He took her hands into his and together, they slowly sat down on the sofa. Marie's eyes fixed on the radio as her dream kept replaying in her head:

*NEW YORK STATE TROOPERS CLAD IN RIOT HEL-
METS AND STANDARD BUT I.D.-LESS UNIFORMS BEGAN
TO FLOOD THE YARD TRYING TO BRING THE MADDEN-
ING SCENE UNDER CONTROL....*

The yard was filled with clouds of white smoke from the
tear gas. Bodies began to fall. Tony's detail moved out onto A-
Catwalk as gunfire erupted around them.

Things were happening fast.

Tony stepped over many bloody bodies in search of his
brother and the other hostages. His Ithaca Model 37 shotgun
was about glued to his hands out of fear of dropping it. *I do not
want other troopers being killed with my own shotgun if I were
to be overpowered.*

Scanning the rain-soaked yard as droplets chinked against
his mask, Tony picked out a target on C-Catwalk, which was on
a diagonal from him and at least 50 yards away from A-Catwalk.
He zeroed in on the inmate holding a hostage. The hostage was

*Advancing trooper on the catwalk at the start of
the re-taking of Attica Prision on September 13, 1971.*

*Photograph courtesy of
Anthony R. Strollo*

frantically trying to escape from his captor. Tony feared for the hostage's life as he saw the rebel inmate brandishing a knife. Tony could not, of course, recognize the hostage, but he knew he had to take out that inmate to prevent him from murdering the hostage...or one of the troopers. With that thought in mind, Tony took aim with the butt of the shotgun bumping up against his gas mask, as he prepared to pump off a round. At that moment, a fellow trooper tapped Tony's shoulder motioning to him that other troopers were now advancing from that very same direction and to watch his line of fire. Tony gave the thumbs-up sign before quickly dropping to his knees to better support his weapon aiming in the direction of the inmate holding the hostage up on C-Catwalk. Tony proceeded with extreme caution. It was his every intention to protect that hostage at all costs from the overall horror picture unfolding around them.

This was the first time during his three years with the State Police that Tony would have to shoot at a person who was in the process of taking the life of another human being. It was a difficult situation, but Tony knew it had to be done. He had to pick out the enemy target and eliminate him if necessary.

YELLS AND GROANS OF DEATH COULD BE HEARD. THE SMELL OF BLOOD HUNG THICK IN THE AIR....

Through the haze and rain, Tony lost visual contact with the executioner. He then proceeded to quickly scan the smoke-filled, body strewn, chaotic yard. *Where in the hell is Frank?* Things were happening so fast, it was like a scene straight out of some action/adventure movie with Tony right in the middle of the worst scene imaginable. Only unlike the movies, the bodies Tony stepped over were dead, and the blood was real. No props here. This was the real thing, grisly and gruesome. No Hollywood movie scene to wrap up. When this real-life drama ends, it was going to be in body bags and on stretchers.

Tony kept his head down low as he ran in a crouched position over the catwalk, stepping over several bloodied and motionless bodies. From the looks of the wounds and the empty glazed expressions in their eyes, Tony knew they were already dead. There was nothing he could do for them except say a prayer when it was all over.

The choppy whir of helicopter blades slicing the air overhead sounded above the shouts and screams of chaos from the yard. A voice sounded over the bullhorn, "Release the hostages. Throw up your hands. Give up. Turn yourself in to the nearest officer and you will not be harmed."

Tony checked out the scene in the yard below. From what he could see, none of the rebel inmates were complying with the order to turn themselves in. Tony knew they were dealing with bold, hard-core inmate ring leaders who were intent on remaining in control of the institution. He knew they probably believed they were dying for a cause.

Tony proceeded with caution, ready for any advancing inmates. As he scouted the area, there were no other inmates standing up on the catwalk . He advanced through a barbwire barricade and was in the process of studying a second one when another large trooper joined him. He tapped on his chest indicating the bullet-proof vest then motioned with his hand to the barricade. Tony nodded in understanding as the other trooper positioned his body across the barbwire using his vest for protection as Tony and the other troopers stepped on his back using it as a springboard, enabling them to get over the barricade.

Continuing on, Tony's breathing became heavier as he frantically searched for his brother. Beads of sweat coated his face and neck, but he couldn't wipe his brow with the gas mask on. Tony scanned the motionless bodies sprawled out on the catwalk, praying that none of them was Frank. A chill shot through him as he stepped over one particular hostage body who had his

Ladder from catwalk to D-Yard   *Photograph by Roy W. Clark*

throat slashed. Tony stared briefly as the blood oozed from the wound. He knew the man. *His poor family*. Tony knew there was absolutely nothing he could do for that C.O. since the man was obviously dead. Hesitating only for the briefest of moments, Tony wished the guy was still alive. He would have given anything to be giving the man safe passage out of the yard. But for that C.O., it was too late.

Tony stepped over many bloodsoaked bodies sprawled out on the catwalk. He swallowed hard, fighting the nausea he suddenly felt. He knew so many of the men. Tony had worked with some, lived next door to some, and attended church with others. Their children went to school together.

Now those men were dead.

Tony located a ladder that led down into D-Yard. Descending the ladder with great speed, he darted through the yard, jumping the muddy trench the inmates had dug. He was still running as he conducted another visual search for Frank and any other hostages he could locate. Tony's breathing became labored, but he could not stop running. He had to keep on moving through the yard. He began to lose his breath and as he reached up to rip off his gas mask, a sudden flashback hit him.

Tony had been engaged in a military training exercise at Fort Dix, New Jersey when they dropped tear gas. Tony, fearing he was losing his breath as a sense of claustrophobia overcame him, reached up and ripped off his gas mask. The second it was off, Tony was overcome by the gas and began choking. He dropped his M-14 as he panicked and ran. His drill instructor, Sergeant Ramos*, was a real hard-ass who was extremely pissed off that one of his soldiers would do such a stupid thing. And he nailed Tony on it, but good.

"You asshole, Strollo!" he hollered. "That'll get you killed and the other guys with you in combat." The sergeant stood directly in front of Tony, who was bent over in absolute misery, choking and gasping for air.

"Pick up your damned rifle, *now!*" he barked the command.

Tony had tried to suck in air to clear his lungs, but only managed to cough and gasp some more as he bent down to pick up his weapon.

Now here Tony was, in the midst of a riot, and he almost made the same mistake. Tony dropped his hand off the gas mask and made a conscious effort to slow his breathing down to a more normal pace. *Thank you, Sergeant Ramos.* Tony then proceeded to search the yard for his brother and other surviving hostages at a more even speed.

Approaching the area of D-Yard, Tony continued his search mission. He came across a trooper who had his shotgun held steadily on a hostage dressed in inmate clothing. The hostage had his hands held straight up in the air.

"Stay put. Do *not* move. Do *not* advance toward me. Stay where you are," the trooper ordered, his voice muffled by the gas mask. Tony, having recognized the hostage as a C.O. he had worked with at one time, jogged over to them.

"It's okay," Tony advised the trooper. "He's one of the hostages! He's one of the hostages!" Tony turned to the C.O. "Where's my brother? Where's Frank?"

The hostage guard glanced around the body-sprawled yard. The troopers were now in control. The inmates choking from the gas, were trying to run, while others overcome by the gas fell to the ground. "He's around here someplace, Tony," the C.O. stated. "I'll help you find him."

The two carefully checked out the area where the hostage circle had been. They saw hostages with inmate bodies piled up on top of them. A sudden jolt shot through Tony as he recognized one particular body lying motionless on the ground. It was his brother, Frank.

Rushing over to him, Tony noted that he was blindfolded. Tony felt tears sting his eyes as he thought for sure Frank was dead as he bent down to try and move him. "Come on," he cried. "Get up!" Tony yelled through the mask as he tried to pull his brother up by his arm.

But Frank did not move.

Finally, Tony leaned over and slowly removed the blindfold. His heart pounded in his chest as he stared down at his brother's lifeless form lying in the mud.

Suddenly, Frank's eyes narrowly flickered open. He then fully recognized who was pulling on him. It was not some inmate executioner, but his own brother backed up by the New York State Police. Tony felt his own body finally relax as a grin spread across his face. He saw relief in his brother's eyes as well.

"I can't move," Frank announced. "My hands and feet are tied."

Tony stared at his brother for a long moment. He thought he would never see his brother alive again, let alone hear his voice. Tony turned and yelled to the other troopers, "He's alive! My brother is alive!"

Several other troopers rushed over and one cut the strips of sheets that bound Frank's hands and feet with his knife. Frank was finally about to be free!

Tony and another trooper each grabbed one of Frank's arms and quickly rushed him through the chaos of D-Yard. They reached the ladders that ascended to the catwalk, and Tony climbed up one and Frank the other as the fellow trooper waited at the bottom until the two brothers had reached the top.

"I REMEMBER SEEING YOU GO UP OVER A WALL...THE PRISON WALL . . . ."

Tony and Frank were met at the top of the catwalk by a State Police Investigator who escorted the two out of the prison to where several ambulances were standing by.

Ladders down into D-Yard from catwalk at Attica State Prison, September 13, 1971. It was on one of these ladders that Trooper Strollo took his hostage-held brother to safety.

Photograph courtesy of Anthony R. Strollo

Aftermath of Riot   D-Yard   *Photographs courtesy of Anthony R. Strollo*

Tony felt exhilarated...to see his brother walk out of the prison...to be alive!

Tony helped his brother into one of the ambulances. They exchanged looks of relief and deep fraternal love before the ambulance technicians closed the vehicle's back doors. Tony turned to head back to the prison, but paused a moment to watch as the ambulance carrying his brother pulled away and headed down the road toward the hospital. A great sigh of relief escaped him as he turned back around and was greeted by scores of happy people who had been waiting days outside the prison for some good news. They didn't even seem to care that it had been raining. Some of the people were soaked, others held umbrellas. But they all had the same expression...one of relief that the insurrection was *finally* over.

The prison chaplain, Father Browning approached Tony. "God bless you, my son," he announced as he patted Tony on the back.

"Thank you, Father," replied Tony. "I believe He already has." Tony smiled a moment as he wiped at the shield of his gas mask with the back of his hand. "I'm going back in to help out," he said as he motioned toward the prison with a nod of his head. "See you later, Father."

Upon re-entering the yard, Tony took in the scene as it was much less chaotic now with the State Police in definite control of the situation. Troopers both in the yard and up on the catwalk were trying to separate the hostages from the inmates. Tony knew his task would now be much easier for the burden of his brother's well-being had been lifted off his shoulders. Tony could continue doing his job knowing that Frank was safely tucked inside the ambulance and enroute to the hospital and his family.

* * *

Back home, Marie had just hung up the telephone. A smile spread across her face as she glanced upward. "Thank you! Thank you!" she exclaimed joyfully.

A.J. and Michael came running into the room. "Was that Daddy, Mommy?" asked A.J..

"Dad-dee"' giggled Michael.

"Is he coming home now?" A.J. hung onto Marie's leg.

Marie bent down and with a fresh surge of energy, she scooped up both boys, hugging them heartily. "That was your Aunt, boys. Daddy will be home *very* soon," she replied before giving each son a kiss on the cheek.

* * *

In D-Yard, there was still a lot of confusion especially around the hostage circle area as the men were still trying to separate hostage from inmate, this task made difficult due to the switched clothing. Tony had an edge over most of the guys because of his former days as a C.O. at Attica, thereby enabling him to distinguish hostage from inmate.

There was a Corrections Lieutenant who had been held hostage, working right alongside Tony and the troopers trying to help. Tony paused a moment to watch the man in awe. Here was a man who not only had been taken hostage, but he sustained obvious injuries during the riot and without having had any medical attention, he jumped right in to assist with getting things back under control in the yard. And the Lieutenant did all that without the benefit of a gas mask.

Tony continued to assist in searching for any weapons. The shooting had subsided and the confusion was beginning to clear. But the facility and grounds were a mess. So much had to be cleaned up. The carnage in D-Yard was beyond words. There were many bloodied bodies to be removed.

Trooper Anthony Strollo - Catwalk Above "Times Square" Attica Prison - 1971   *Photograph by*
Roy W. Clark

Tony shook his head wondering what had been accomplished by the riot. Nothing short of creating a disaster. Men were dead; both hostages and inmates. That was the only thing accomplished. Men had lost their lives. Families will grieve. And all for what?

After escorting some inmates back to their cellblocks, the Lieutenant approached Tony. It was about 2:00 p.m.

"I understand you got your brother out alive," Lieutenant Arthur announced. "Nice job."

Tony nodded his thanks.

"So what are you still doing here? You should be out of here. You should be with your brother visiting the family. I want you out of here." Lieutenant Arthur spotted an investigator who was not busy at that moment. He walked over to him, knowing he

Helicopter on the prison grounds   *Photograph courtesy of Anthony R. Strollo*

was also familiar with the Batavia area where Frank Strollo resided. "Take Tony to his brother's house in Batavia. We just got
word that he has been treated and released from the hospital,
so Tony's off for the rest of the day. If anybody wants him, he'll
be over at his brother's."

"Thank you," Tony replied wearily before leaving the prison
in the company of the investigator.

Once outside the prison walls, they approached one of the
waiting B.C.I. cars and slid into the front seat. Soaking wet and
tired, Tony leaned his head back on the seat and closed his eyes.
Totally wiped out, he didn't even bother to remove his riot helmet. Emotionally, everything was beginning to hit him at that
very moment. Scenes from the past four days played out in his
head. For as long as he lived, Tony knew he would never forget
seeing his brother's motionless body lying sprawled out on the
damp, wet ground of D-Yard.

As the car pulled away from the institution, Tony opened
his eyes and watched Attica pass from view. When it was com-

pletely out of sight, Tony dropped his glance to the side-view mirror and saw the formidable Attica prison looming over the lawns where hundreds of people waited as troopers escorted all the injured out into the waiting ambulances. Armed C.O.s stood nearby waiting to accompany injured inmates to the hospital. Tony saw the helicopters now quietly parked on the lawns as a cloud of tear gas still hung over the entire prison, giving it an eerie, almost surreal effect. When the institution was completely out of the mirror's view, Tony did not bother to turn around for a last look. Instead, he closed his eyes and hoped he would never have to return to Attica again... but knew full well, if his job required him to do so, he would.

The investigator turned the car down Frank's street. As Tony opened his bloodshot eyes, he saw so many cars parked up and down the street that it resembled a block party. As the investigator parked the car, Tony wondered if someone thought to call Marie and give her the good news. He knew she would be waiting to hear. Tony decided that he would phone her himself just as soon as he could make his way through the masses of relatives, friends and neighbors who flooded Frank's front porch.

Tony slid out of the B.C.I. car and removed his helmet, running a hand through his matted hair. Tossing the helmet on the seat, he shut the door and walked up onto the porch. The crowd of people parted, allowing him to pass through as they reached out to either shake his hand or pat him on the back. Tony vaguely heard them offering their congratulations. He really was not listening to them. He just wanted to see his brother.

Once inside the house, Tony spotted Frank still clad in inmate clothing and sporting several days growth of beard as he stood in his living room hugging his wife, eight-year old son and five-year old daughter. Their parents stood nearby. Tony saw the tears of joy that filled their eyes and had to fight back crying himself. The house was packed with well-wishers. Tony stopped in the midst of all the people to just look at his brother. At that moment, Frank glanced up and saw Tony. They stood there apart for a long moment, then rushed across the crowded room to tightly embrace each other.

"Frank!" Tony exclaimed as he hugged his brother.

"Anthony!"

Tony and Frank clung to each other for a long time. Tears of joy and relief filled their eyes. The four long days had finally come to a close.

For the Strollo family it had a miraculously happy ending. But for many families who had loved ones involved in Attica, it was not so joyous. Tony knew he had lucked out. As he held onto his brother, he glanced upward to offer his silent prayer of thanks.

* * *

"Somebody up there must have been looking over me, boy, 'cause I'll tell you I came close to death. So did everybody else there..my hat goes off to the other troopers who were there because everyone who was there risked their life. And they did a hell of a job. I knew my mind was made up. We were going into Attica knowing the hostages' lives were at stake...including my own brother's. I also knew that the chances were slim that they would get out of there alive. It was a hostile situation. You just try to do the best job possible.

That's all anyone can expect."

Anthony R. Strollo

The following retrospection is an excerpt from former Commissioner of Corrections Russell G. Oswald's book, *Attica - My Story*:

A (State Police) Lieutenant, second in command of the rescue squad, was the leader of the charge toward the hostages. He ran through the gas, rain and gunsmoke toward (the) men. He saw one about to be clubbed by an inmate and told the man to drop the club. Then he ordered all the inmates and hostages in the area to drop to the ground.

Now came the single event causing most casualties at Attica. One of the rebels grabbed (the) Lieutenant by the leg, and (the) Lieutenant lost his balance and fell. Somehow he managed to twist himself in falling and he was able to land on top of his shotgun. At all costs (the) firearms had to be kept out of the hands of the inmates. As he lay on the ground, he was struck on the head with a club, fortunately his helmet protected him from injury. One of the rebels yelled jubilantly.... "I got one of them!"

At once, a fellow officer opened fire to protect (the) Lieutenant, killing the man who had downed him. One or two other troopers overlooking D-Yard opened up in support. But each of the shotgun shells was loaded with ten pellets, and they had a spray effect on the crowd of inmates and hostages in D-Yard. (The) Lieutenant himself was struck twice, in the arm and the leg. He was one of the six State Troopers wounded in the assault.

Here, then, was the vortex of the battle, with gunfire now coming in from several directions into a densely populated target area. The rebels making their strongest stand and the hostages attempting to break free were all now in deadly danger. Here it was, from shotgun and other gunfire wounds, that seven of our hostages were killed - and another would later die of his wounds. Many of the hostages, injured during the uprising, were wounded again. Many of the 29 inmates killed on September 13 fell in this brief...encounter.

But here it was also that most of our hostages were rescued. It was heart-rending that we were to lose eight hostages in this phase of the struggle, but we saved twenty-two hostages in this same D-Yard melee and that was almost miraculous in the circumstances.

There was no way our sharpshooters could have picked off executioners in the crowded yard as expeditiously as they had done at Times Square.

If they had found their marks, then other rebels would have surely killed the hostages where they stood. There was no other way - a rescue squad had to move right into D-Yard to save our men.

Inevitably, perhaps, the very lead officer moving against hundreds of men, disabled even though they were by CS gas, was going to meet resistance. This one man was the pinpoint of the whole rescue mission. His life was saved by his comrades. His weapon was also saved. If the rebels had obtained a shotgun, they would have been able to knock out others in the rescue squad, take their shotguns and inflict heavy casualties on the troops.

(A) Corrections officer Captain who had risked his life to help (a) Lieutenant at the beginning of the rebellion: "I was in the front rank, dressed in an inmate shirt, buttoned, hands tied in front, and my feet tied. I was standing with an inmate behind me, with his hand on my throat. There was the blast of gas. The inmate told me to drop. I stayed put on the ground, my blindfold partially pushed up. I saw three troopers and yelled for help, and they cut me loose. I went with the troopers to help identify hostages. I climbed the ladder to the roof and walked all the way to the ambulance."

One civilian hostage said, "The man behind me, my executioner who had a hold of my back, said he'd stop my feet from shaking soon. He tapped me on the back three or four times with a weapon. I heard the leader order not to kill anybody until one of them died. 'If we die, you die!'"...Then I was knocked to the ground after being hit in the side, probably by gunshot.

"*After I got hit, somebody kept tugging at me, trying to get me up on my feet. He did get me up on my feet. My hands and feet were still tied. He straightened me up. I felt a knife sawing away at the binding between my hands and feet. I can only assume this was an inmate.*

"*As soon as the bindings came apart, I stood up, leaped forward, tried to push myself out of there still blindfolded. I must have travelled about fifteen feet. Somebody grabbed me from behind, yanked my blindfold off then I saw the brightest and shiniest boots I ever saw - a trooper.*"

Corrections Officer Frank Strollo told Newsweek that he was hit on the back of the head with a length of pipe when the firing began: "*Whoever did it, he sort of got on top of me. I heard guys saying, 'Don't kill him, don't kill him!'*"

(An) Industrial Foreman: "*An executioner was at my back and jabbed something into my back. I was sure they were going to burn us up. Something started hitting the ground as a helicopter passed over, and I threw myself on the ground, and my hands became loose and I removed the blindfold.*

"*Someone hit me on the head and dazed me, but I saw an inmate trying to pull me up and he had a pipe, and I grabbed it from him and hit him on the head, and he went down.*

"*I then saw a trooper and identified myself, and I was helped out of the yard. I had received a hairline fracture of the skull and a broken rib.*"

(A C.O.) Lieutenant, still standing, suddenly felt a terrific jolt right in the center of his back. This knocked the wind out of him and threw him to his knees, and at the same time a voice behind him shouted, "*They're shooting - I'm shot.*" *When he*

heard this, he pushed up his blindfold, looked back, and saw a man's hand on his shoulder with a hole in the back of the hand. Then he saw the New York State Police - "the men from Mars, and God bless them." They were still some ten feet short of him, so (the) Lieutenant dove toward them, his hands and feet still tied, and he rolled over on the ground until he was safe."

(A C.O.) Captain recalls, "We could hear the helicopter. The first gas canister went off. I heard a shot. The man holding me pressed the knife into my neck and suddenly he was gone. The bullet went right past my neck - missed it by an inch. There was a loud explosion. I don't know what it was, but...it hit me a blow on the back of the head, knocked me down and I lost consciousness.

"...I woke up in the middle of it all. I was still blindfolded and tied. I could hear voices. Thought the inmates were all around me. I thought they'd kill me if I moved. I moved the bandage off my eyes and saw the biggest trooper. He said, 'My God, we've been looking all over for you.'"

1972   *Attica-My Story*
Doubleday & Co., Inc.   Russell G. Oswald

*The prison keys taken on first day of riot
later found in D-Yard were buried
under this monument.*

Photograph by
Donald E. Skinner

Monument erected in memory of the employees who gave their lives in the riot. May we never forget those who made the ultimate sacrifice.

Photograph by Donald E. Skinner

AFTERWORD

* * *

When the riot was over and the rescue/retaking detail complete, 38 men were dead including 10 hostages. An 11th died weeks later in a hospital as a result of injuries sustained during the hostile takeover of the prison by the rebel inmates.

29 hostages had been rescued.

Trooper Anthony Strollo retired from the New York State Police as a Sergeant with over 20 years of service. He and his wife, Marie, still reside in New York State. In addition to being an author, Tony has been an Adjunct Professor of Criminal Justice, and owns a family-run business.

Frank Strollo was the first hostage to return to duty as a Correctional Officer at Attica after the riot. He is still a Correctional Officer for the state of New York.

The losses on both sides, if there are indeed sides, have been enormous, the death, almost unspeakable. Many who survived the Attica ordeal have carried an unbearable burden, even to the grave.

The record stands. If we have not learned, we are doomed to repeat history.

1987   *History of the New York State*
New York   *Police 1917 - 1987.*
                              "Attica - 1971 - LeBastille
                              Extraordinaire"
                              Sgt. Pamela T. Shelton

132

A "home made" type rocket launcher put together by inmates during their four days of control. Fortunately, the device did not work.

Photograph courtesy of Anthony R. Strollo

Some of the various weapons recovered from rioting inmates on September 13, 1971 when State Police re-took control of Attica Prision.

Photographs courtesy of Anthony R. Strollo

Return to Attica - *Strollo present day in front of the facility*

Photograph By
Rocco Laurienzo
Batavia Daily News

EPILOGUE

Present

* * *

"Do you have everything prepared for the first day of class, Tony?" Marie asked as she read over a letter she received from their oldest son, A.J., who resided out of state.

"Mmm-hmm," Tony replied as he snapped shut his brief case. "All set." Tony glanced over at his wife as he took a sip of coffee from the mug sitting before him on the kitchen table. "So what does A.J. have to say?"

Marie carefully folded the letter and placed it down on the table. "Oh, he really likes it out there. Lots of sunshine. Lots of pretty girls. The usual." She smiled up at Tony. "So, what are you going to talk about today, Professor?"

Tony refilled his mug, then sat down on the chair across the table from his wife. "The usual," he grinned. "I'm going to discuss what I expect from them during the semester...what issues we will cover...."

"Attica?" The question hung in the air a moment before Tony responded.

He nodded. "Of course, Attica. But that's not the only thing. We'll examine the Criminal Justice system from *all* aspects. From the courts, the police—"

"The prisons," Marie finished for him as she studied her husband over her mug of coffee.

Tony grinned. Sometimes he forgot just how well she knew

him. "Yes, and from the prisons. Especially since the twenty-fifth anniversary of the riot is not all that far off. Attica is a piece of history, Marie. I know how emotionally traumatic it was for all of us involved. For you, too. But forty-three people died as a result of Attica. And why did they die? The riot was a great tragedy for many families, yet many people will forget the bloodiest prison riot in American history. But for others...it will never be forgotten."

Tony turned his attention out their window to watch the fluffy white snowflakes that began to float down from the gray sky above. "It's my job to make sure they don't forget." He turned to his wife. "Besides, I believe that maybe, just maybe if we in some way keep them aware of what happened at Attica, maybe we can prevent another one from ever occurring."

Tony stood up and finished his coffee. "Don't forget, Hon. We're dealing with a whole new generation now. Some of those kids don't even know what Attica is." As Tony draped his coat over his arm, Marie walked around the table and adjusted his tie.

"Have a good day, Professor Strollo," she said as she wrapped her arm around him.

Tony bent over and kissed Marie before heading over to the community college for a day of classes.

Yes, he would indeed talk to them about his experiences at Attica. Almost twenty-five years ago Tony had made a promise to never allow himself to forget the vision of Frank lying motionless on the ground of D-Yard. Not that he ever could. There were still sleepless nights when the Attica riot haunted Tony's dreams. He knew never in a million years would he forget how it felt to be a part of the hostage rescue detail as he stepped over the bloody and dead bodies of former co-workers and friends.

Yes, Tony. how do you feel? The words from his past echoed in his mind.

It did not matter whether it was the 25th, 30th or 50th anniversary of the Attica Riot. For as long as he was alive, Tony would *never* forget.

THE END

CLOSING STATEMENT

"Attica, September 13, 1971, was the day long to be remembered. Many families lost loved ones: Guards, Inmates, Fathers, Sons, Husbands, Brothers, Cousins.... They all had a position in life. Life that is so precious in many ways. Why did it have to end? Families endured much stress from anticipation while anxiously waiting to hear about their loved ones. Many of these individuals and families have changed their view of life as a result of the riot. Even if a life was only touched by the Attica Riot, those Four Long Days *will never be forgotten. We must continue to search for the answers and find ways to make the system work for the benefit of all. No one wants another Attica."*

1993   Anthony R. Strollo
New York

New York State Trooper Anthony R. Strollo   *Photograph courtesy of Anthony R. Strollo*

Appendix A

STATE OF NEW YORK
EXECUTIVE CHAMBER
ALBANY 12224

NELSON A. ROCKEFELLER
GOVERNOR

October 6, 1971

Dear Trooper Strollo:

During the Attica Prison uprising, no role was more important, or more perilous, than the one you performed as a member of the rescue unit that reentered the prison on the morning of September thirteenth.

Because of the courage and professional skill of you and other members of the unit, the rescue mission succeeded in saving the lives of 28 of the 38 hostages and in quelling the largest prison riot in American history, with loss of life held far below the terrible potential of this desperate situation.

After all the difficult decisions had been made, it was you and your fellow officers who had to face the ultimate peril. You did so in a manner reflecting great credit on yourselves and the traditions of the New York State Police.

Sincerely,

Trooper A. R. Strollo
Troop E
New York State Police
Canandaigua, New York 14424

Appendix B

NEW YORK STATE DEPARTMENT OF CORRECTIONAL
SERVICES NUMBER OF FACILITES AS OF JUNE 30, 1994
(Courtesy of N.Y.S. Department of
Correctional Services, Albany, New York)

FACILITY AND SECURITY LEVEL	COUNTY LOCATED	DATE OPENED	MINIMUM SECURITY UNIT OF A PREVIOUSLY LISTED FACILITY
ALL FACILITIES	*67 FACILITIES*		
MAXIMUM. SECURITY- MALE	*14 FACILITIES*		
ATTICA	WYOMING	1931	
AUBURN	CAYUGA	1817	
CLINTON	CLINTON	1845	
COXSACKIE	GREENE	1935	
DOWNSTATE	DUTCHESS	1979	
EASTERN	ULSTER	1900	
ELMIRA	CHEMUNG	1876	
GREAT MEADOW	WASHINGTON	1911	
GREEN HAVEN	DUTCHESS	1949	
SHAWANGUNK	ULSTER	JAN 1986	
SING SING	WESTCHESTER	1825	
SOUTHPORT	CHEMUNG	OCT 1988	
SULLIVAN	SULLIVAN	JUL 1985	
WENDE	ERIE	NOV 1983	

MEDIUM SECURITY- MALE	*33 FACILITIES*		**MEDIUM SECURITY UNIT OF A PREVIOUSLY LISTED FACILITY**
ADIRONDACK	ESSEX	1976	EASTERN ANNEX
ALTONA	CLINTON	APR 1983	(Eastern-Maximum)
ARTHURKILL	RICHMOND	1976	GREEN HAVEN ANNEX
BARE HILL	FRANKLIN	NOV 1988	(Green Haven- Minimum)
BUTLER(ASACTC)	WAYNE	JUN 1989	SING SING
CAPE VINCENT	JEFFERSON	APR 1993	(Sing Sing - Maximum)
CAYUGA	CAYUGA	NOV 1988	MARCY ASACTC
CHATEAUGAY(ASACTC)	CLINTON	AUG 1990	(Marcy-Medium)
COLLINS	ERIE	1982	
FISHKILL	DUTCHESS	1892	
FRANKLIN	FRANKLIN	AUG 1986	
GOUVERNEUR	ST. LAWRENCE	OCT 1990	
GREENE	GREENE	OCT 1984	
GROVELAND	LIVINGSTON	DEC 1982	
HALE CREEK (ASACTC)	FULTON	OCT 1990	
HUDSON	COLUMBIA	1976	
LIVINGSTON	LIVINGSTON	JAN 1991	
GOWANDA	ERIE	AUG 1994	

FACILITY AND SECURITY LEVEL Cont'd	COUNTY LOCATED	DATE OPENED	MINIMUM SECURITY UNIT OF A PREVIOUSLY LISTED FACILITY
MARCY	ONEIDA	DEC 1988	
MID ORANGE	ORANGE	1977	
MID STATE	ONEIDA	JAN 1984	
MOHAWK	ONEIDA	NOV 1989	
MT. MCGREGOR	SARATOGA	1976	
OGDENSBURG	ST. LAWRENCE	1982	
ONEIDA	ONEIDA	JAN 1988	
ORLEANS	ORLEANS	JAN 1985	
OTISVILLE	ORANGE	1977	
RIVERVIEW	ST. LAWRENCE	NOV 1992	
ULSTER	ULSTER	OCT 1990	
WALLKILL	ULSTER	1932	
WASHINGTON	WASHINGTON	MAR 1985	
WATERTOWN	JEFFERSON	1982	
WOODBOURNE	SULLIVAN	1935	
WYOMING	WYOMING	DEC 1984	

FACILITY AND SECURITY LEVEL	COUNTY LOCATED	DATE OPENED	MINIMUM SECURITY UNIT OF A PREVIOUSLY LISTED FACILITY
MINIMUM (OTHER) - MALE	*5 FACILITIES*		
LAKEVIEW	CHAUTAUQUA	AUG 1989	BUTLER
LYON MT.	CLINTON	FEB 1984	(BUTLER ASACTC - Med.)
MONTEREY	SCHUYLER	1958	FALLSBURG ANNEX
MORIAH	ESSEX	MAR 1989	(SULLIVAN - Medium)
SUMMIT	SCHOHARIE	1961	GROVELAND
			(GROVELAND - Medium)
MINIMUM (WK REL) - MALE	*6 FACILITIES*		
BUFFALO	ERIE	JUL 1992	FISHKILL W.R.
EDGECOMBE	NEW YORK	1974	(FISHKILL - Medium)
FULTON	BRONX	1976	HUDSON W.R.
LINCOLN	NEW YORK	1976	(HUDSON - Medium)
QUEENSBORO	QUEENS	1976	ORLEANS W.R.
ROCHESTER	MONROE	1973	(ORLEANS - Medium)
MINIMUM (CAMPS) - MALE	*3 FACILITIES*		
CAMP GABRIEL	FRANKLIN	1982	CAMP MT. MCGREGOR
CAMP GEORGETOWN	MADISON	1961	
CAMP PHARSALIA	CHENANGO	1956	

FACILITY AND SECURITY LEVEL	COUNTY LOCATED	DATE OPENED	MINIMUM SECURITY UNIT OF A PREVIOUSLY LISTED FACILITY
FEMALES	*6 FACILITIES*		
ALBION (Medium)	ORLEANS	1977	LAKEVIEW
BAYVIEW (Medium)	NEW YORK	1974	(Minimum - Male)
BEDFORD HILL (Max.)	WESTCHESTER	1933	
BEACON (Minimum)	DUTCHESS	1982	
PARKSIDE (Min.)	NEW YORK	1975	
TACONIC (Medium)	WESTCHESTER	1933	

NOTES:
Total number of facilities is as if Butler (minimum) is counted as a separate facility

144

Appendix C

NEW YORK STATE MALE CORRECTIONAL FACILITIES
(Courtesy of N.Y.S. Department of Correctional Services)

MAXIMUM SECURITY

ATTICA CORRECTIONAL FACILITY (Wyoming County)
AUBURN CORRECTIONAL FACILITY (Cayuga County)
CLINTON CORRECTIONAL FACILITY (Clinton County)
COXSACKIE CORRECTIONAL FACILITY (Greene County)
DOWNSTATE CORRECTIONAL FACILITY (Dutchess County)
EASTERN CORRECTIONAL FACILITY (Ulster County)
ELMIRA CORRECTIONAL FACILITY (Chemung County)
GREEN HAVEN CORRECTIONAL FACILITY (Dutchess County)
GREAT MEADOW CORRECTIONAL FACILITY (Washington County)
SHAWANGUNK CORRECTIONAL FACILITY (Ulster County)
SING SING CORRECTIONAL FACILITY (Westerchester County)
WENDE CORRECTIONAL FACILITY (Erie County)

MEDIUM SECURITY

ADIRONDACK CORRECTIONAL FACILITY (Clinton County)
ALTONA CORRECTIONAL FACILITY (Clinton County)
ARTHURKILL CORRECTIONAL FACILITY & CASAT (Richmond County)
BARE HILL CORRECTIONAL FACILITY (Franklin County)
BUTLER COMPREHENSIVE ALCOHOL & SUBSTANCE
   ABUSE TREATMENT (CASAT) (WayneCounty)
CAPE VINCENT CORRECTIONAL FACILTIY & CASAT (Jefferson County)
CAYUGA CORRECTIONAL FACILITY (Cayuga County)
CHATEAUGAY CASAT (Franklin County)
COLLINS CORRECTIONAL FACILITY (Erie County)
FISHKILL CORRECTIONAL FACILITY (Dutchess County)
FRANKLIN CORRECTIONAL FACILITY (Franklin County)
GOUVERNEUR CORRECTIONAL FACILITY (St. Lawrence County)
GREEN CORRECTIONAL FACILITY (Greene County)
GROVELAND CORRECTIONAL FACILITY (Livingston County)
HALE CREEK CASAT (Fulton County)
HUDSON CORRECTIONAL FACILITY (Columbia County)
LIVINGSTON CORRECTIONAL FACILITY (Livingston County)
MARCY CORRECTIONAL FACILITY & CASAT ANNEX (Oneida County)
MID-ORANGE CORRECTIONAL FACILITY (Orange County)
MID-STATE CORRECTIONAL FACILITY (Oneida County)
MOHAWK CORRECTIONAL FACILITY (Oneida County)
MT. MCGREGOR CORRECTIONAL FACILITY (Saratoga County)
OGDENSBURG CORRECTIONAL FACILITY (St. Lawrenece County)

ONEIDA CORRECTIONAL FACILITY (Oneida County)
ORLEANS CORRECTIONAL FACILITY (Orleans County)
OTISVILLE CORRECTIONAL FACILITY (Orange County)
RIVERVIEW CORRECTIONAL FACILITY (St. Lawrence County)
ULSTER CORRECTIONAL FACILITY (Ulster County)
WALKILL CORRECTIONAL FACILITY (Ulster County)
WASHINGTON CORRECTIONAL FACILITY (Washington County)
WATERTOWN CORRECTIONAL FACILITY (Jefferson County)
WOODBOURNE CORRECTIONAL FACILITY (Sullivan County)
WYOMING CORRECTIONAL FACILITY (Wyoming County)

MINIMUM SECURITY

BUTLER CORRECTIONAL FACILITY (Wayne County)
LYON MOUNTAIN CORRECTIONAL FACILITY (Clinton County)

MINIMUM WORK RELEASE

BUFFALO CORRECTIONAL FACILITY (Erie County)
EDGECOMBE CORRECTIONAL FACILITY (New York County)
*FISHKILL CORRECTIONAL FACILITY (Dutchess County)
FULTON CORRECTIONAL FACILITY (Bronx County)
*HUDSON CORRECTIONAL FACILITY (Columbia County)
LINCOLN CORRECTIONAL FACILITY (New York County)
QUEENSBORO CORRECTIONAL FACILITY (Queens County)
ROCHESTER CORRECTIONAL FACI~LITY (Monroe County)

CAMPS

CAMP GARBIEL (Franklin County)
CAMP GEORGETOWN (Madison County)
CAMP MT. MCGREGOR (Saratoga County)
CAMP PHARSALIA (Chenango County)

SHOCK INCARCERATION

LAKEVIEW SHOCK INCARCERATION FACILITY (Chautauqua County)
MONTEREY SHOCK INCARCERATION FACILITY (Schuyler County)
MORIAH SHOCK INCARCERATION FACILITY (Essex County)
SUMMIT SHOCK INCARCERATION FACILITY (Schoharie County)

*Only a portion of these general confinement facilities are work release beds.

Appendix D

NEW YORK STATE FEMALE CORRECTIONAL FACILITIES
(Courtesy of N.Y.S. Department of Correctional Services)

MAXIMUM SECURITY

BEDFORD HILLS CORRECTIONAL FACILITY (Westchester County)

MEDIUM SECURITY

ALBION CORRECTIONAL FACILITY (Orleans County)
BAYVIEW CORRECTIONAL FACILITY (New York County)
TACONIC CORRECTIONAL FACILITY & CASAT (Westchester County)

MINIMUM SECURITY

BEACON CORRECTIONAL FACILITY (Dutchess County)

MINIMUM WORK RELEASE

*ALBION CORRECTIONAL FACILITY (Orleans County)
*BAYVIEW CORRECTIONAL FACILITY (New York County)
PARKSIDE CORRECTIONAL FACILITY (New York County)

SHOCK INCARCERATION

LAKEVIEW SHOCK INCARCERATION FACILITY (Chautauqua County)

*Only a portion of these general confinement facilities are work release beds.

Bibliography

Excerpts throughout the book have been reprinted with permission from the following publications.

New York Times, The. "The Attica Revolt: Hour-By-Hour". New York: The New York Times Company; Joseph Lelyveld, Francis X. Clines, Michael T. Kaufmann and James M. Markham, October 4, 1971.

Attica - My Story. Oswald, Russell G. New York: Doubleday & Company, Inc., 1972.

History of the New York State Police 1917 - 1987. "Attica - 1971 - LeBastille Extraordinaire". Shelton, Pamela T., Sgt. New York: The Trooper Foundation the State of New York, 1987.

New York State Department of Correctional Services Number of Facilities, Male and Female Correctional Facilities. New York State Department of Correctional Services, Albany, New York. 1994.